HOUSE
OF A
HUNDRED
DOORS

HOUSE
OF A
HUNDRED
DOORS

SAM SCOTT

The Book Guild Ltd

First published in Great Britain in 2023 by
The Book Guild Ltd
Unit E2 Airfield Business Park,
Harrison Road, Market Harborough,
Leicestershire. LE16 7UL
Tel: 0116 2792299
www.bookguild.co.uk
Email: info@bookguild.co.uk
Twitter: @bookguild

Typeset in 11pt Minion Pro

Printed and bound by CPI Group (UK) Ltd, Croydon, CR0 4YY

ISBN 978 1915352 644

British Library Cataloguing in Publication Data.
A catalogue record for this book is available from the British Library.

For Michael
Soulmates - Together Forever
Sam

PROLOGUE

HACKERS HOLLOW, 1893

"How do you do, sir? It is a pleasure to meet you. Won't you please sit down?" An austere-looking Harrison Hacker indicated the chair in front of his desk.

"Good day, Mr Hacker, the pleasure is mine, and please, the name is Brute. Thank you for seeing me at such short notice." David Brute looked around the dull and featureless room, which housed only a desk, two chairs and a bookcase, filled with medical journals and encyclopaedias. There was an indistinct damp smell that mixed with odours of disinfectant and rotten vegetables. It struck David Brute that, just possibly, it was the smell of death.

"That is quite all right. Your telegram explained the situation. I trust Mrs Brute is with you?"

"Yes, she is waiting in the carriage outside. I thought it best to conduct our business in private, Mr Hacker. Are you able to help me?"

"I believe I can. You wrote that she suffers from constant headaches and seems irrational and paranoid much of the time. These are extremely common conditions, especially in the ladies.

We have many tried, and new, treatments that we can use to help her."

"And she may stay as long as she needs to?"

Harrison Hacker knew exactly what David Brute was asking.

"Most certainly. Indefinitely, if need be. It only takes the signatures of two of my doctors and your wife will be committed. Do you have the payment with you?"

"Yes, indeed, I believe twenty-five thousand dollars was the agreed amount. It is all there." Mr Brute passed a leather attaché case across the desk to Harrison Hacker, with a satisfied yet sadistic look on his face. "It has been a pleasure doing business with you, Mr Hacker."

"And you, Mr Brute. Now, shall we have your wife brought in?"

The two men walked to the front door. Harrison Hacker rang a bell and as David Brute watched the feeble-looking man, he wondered how he handled the patients. Two orderlies, dressed in dirty white lab coats, appeared from a door across the hallway and exited the building towards the waiting Mrs Brute in the horse-drawn carriage outside. Having helped her down, they each took hold of one of her arms and escorted her inside.

"David, what is this place? What are we doing here?" The dazed young woman, with a faraway look in her eyes, seemed confused.

"This is Mr Hacker, Elizabeth. Remember I told you that he could help with your headaches. You are going to stay here with him and the doctors."

"But David, I don't want to stay here. Please take me home."

"Come, come, my dear. Be a good girl. This is your new home. Now, go with the nice gentlemen and they will help you."

As Elizabeth Brute was taken through another of the five doors that led off the entrance foyer, Harrison Hacker and David Brute shook hands to seal their deal. Both men were satisfied with the conclusion. Hacker had another twenty-five thousand dollars to his name. Brute had his problematic wife off his hands, and as he turned and left the building, he smiled as he heard the unmistakable piercing sound of his wife's screams.

PART ONE

THE SET-UP

ONE

2013

A CHANCE MEETING

"Okay, everyone, places. Quiet, please. Screen test. Take one. Action!"

"Good evening, ladies and gentlemen, boys and girls, and welcome to *Pennsylvania*! We are gathered at this ancient gothic-style mansion for an incredibly special, one-off show. Five contestants are in the house, waiting to search the building. And by the end of the night, one of them will be the winner, having located the prize bag of one hundred thousand dollars. Remember, once inside, nothing is as it seems, yet everything seems to be something. So, sit back, relax and come with me, your host – Maximillion Crooked – into the House of a Hundred Doors."

"Cut! Thanks, everyone. Take five. Not bad, Mr Crooked, not bad at all. The camera responds well to you. If you would like to follow me into my office, we can discuss your idea in much greater detail." Muir Mason, the studio owner, seemed pleased.

"Lead the way, Mr Mason, and please, call me Max."

The two men entered the private office, away from the studio crew, and sat down to business. Two men that could not have been more different. Not only in looks, but in nature and ethics.

"So, it is a real house? It's empty? And we can definitely film there?"

"That's right, Mr Mason. It is called Hacker Hall and I first learnt about it from a friend. She talked at great length about it. I was so intrigued, she took me there a few months ago to have a look around. The idea came to me almost instantly on learning the history of the house. I just needed a little time to plan everything out."

"Excellent, Max. We are a small network, so this could work well for both of us. I like the premise of the show and your name, Maximillion Crooked, is perfect for a game show presenter. Now, tell me what you are thinking."

"The house is a maze of interconnecting rooms, with one door leading to another. It covers four floors, from basement to attic, and was once an asylum for the clinically insane. It has been empty and abandoned for almost a hundred years. So, I thought we could air the show live on the 100th anniversary of its closure. We choose five kids, all from quite different backgrounds and put them in the house. They must search from room to room, looking for the bag of prize money."

"And how will they be working? As a team?"

"I have considered that, Mr Mason. Although I believe they will be more thorough as individuals. If they work together, they will have to split the prize money, which offers less of an incentive. But if they are on their own, they will become more competitive and more willing to battle it out."

"Sure thing. And based on the venue, do you have any plans to spice things up once they are inside?"

"Most certainly. Of course, we want one of them to locate the money, but for the sake of good viewing it is our responsibility to make their job as difficult as possible. As they search, they will come across different situations, using every type of special effect to make the house scary and entertaining. There have been rumours for generations that the house may be haunted. So, we can work with that idea."

"I like it. What sort of things do you have in mind?" Muir Mason was already hooked on the idea and revelled in the prospect of his television network producing such a groundbreaking game show.

"Anything from getting trapped to snakes in cupboards. Bumps in the night. Maybe even a gentle poisoning."

"Goodness, Max! I don't think we will need to go that far, but whatever makes good television, I am up for it. Within reason, of course. We are talking about children, you know. What sort of age group were you thinking?"

"Probably twelve to eighteen. As long as we have parental permission, there shouldn't be any problems. Children are adaptable and far more open to the idea of bad things happening. Much more so than adults. All good for bringing audience numbers up. And if you include a phoneline, viewers can call in and vote for who they want to win. That will bring in more cash for the network, too."

"Great. I can't wait to see this place. Do you have any pictures with you?"

"I certainly do," Max replied and placed a series of photographs on the desk.

"It sure is a haunted-looking building." Muir Mason picked up a picture showing the outside of the hall. Then his attention turned to the remaining photographs. "Good God! All the stuff in these pictures, is it still in situ and can be used in the show?" He winced at the sight of the torturous equipment from a past uncivilised time.

"Great, isn't it? Just wait until you get in there. The smell… the eeriness…"

"Yes, Max, I get it. And it really is in Pennsylvania? That is a great touch. Anything that sounds similar to Transylvania causes interest and makes great TV."

"Yes, it is set on the edge of the Pennsylvania State Forest, near a small town called Hackers Hollow. I also thought maybe a live studio audience on the night, set up on the front lawn, would work. I reckon there would be great demand to be at the hall and witness the event live, watching on giant video screens."

"Fantastic. I love it. I would like to make arrangements to get out to the hall for a look around as soon as possible. After that, I will speak to the legal team to sort the permissions to film there. Then, I think we should put out a nationwide advert, calling for contestants." Muir Mason had not been so excited about a programme concept in a long time.

"Good idea. I can help with that. I would like to be involved every step of the way, if you will permit me. I want to be much more than the presenter," Max said.

"Of course, Max. It will be a pleasure to have you on board. I will have a contract drawn up and ready for you to sign. Let's get this show on the road."

Maximillion Crooked towered above Muir Mason as they stood up from the desk and shook hands. Muir agreed to be in touch with Max as soon as he had placed the advertisement for contestants and could get away to visit the hall. He watched Max leave his office and felt a chill run over him. Maximillion Crooked certainly was a character. He had a great idea for a hit television show, but there was something slightly odd that Muir could not pinpoint. It must have been all the talk of the old, supposedly haunted, house. Muir Mason had good instincts about people and with Maximillion Crooked, he was on to a winner.

Max turned up his collar and clasped his jacket tightly around his chest as he left the television studio in New York. As he ran to the waiting car, parked nearby, the rain on the pavement danced around his shoes. He observed the quiet street as he climbed into the passenger seat.

"Well, did he go for it?" Imogen asked and started the engine.

"Oh, yes. He loved the idea. Everything is coming together nicely."

"And you will keep your promise that once this is over, you will leave and I will never see or hear from you again."

"It's a shame. When we met, I felt it was down to some sort of fate and I can see great things for us if we stick together, but a promise is a promise, Imogen. You will never see me again."

The day Imogen met Max had been an upsetting one and the fact she was sitting in a Pennsylvania bar mid-afternoon spoke volumes. The argument with her sister, over lunch, had been one of the worst yet. She had not wanted to go straight home. She did not want her father and mother to see how upset she was. A glass or two of something to calm her nerves seemed to be just what she needed. When Max sat down next to her at the bar, Imogen was already on her third drink and was happy to chat to the stranger who offered a fourth.

Having introduced himself, Imogen remembered laughing at his name. "*Maximillion Crooked*, what sort of name is that? You are kidding, right?" she slurred.

"Go on, then. Is yours any better?"

"Imogen Hackerton. Pleased to meet you."

"Hackerton! That is nearly as bad as Crooked. Hey, wait. Any relation to Emerson Hackerton?" Max recognised the name instantly as the family name of the popular congressman who was in the running to be next Senator of Pennsylvania.

"Yes, indeedie. He is my father. Do you know him?"

"No, but I know he is a very well-liked man. So, what's this all about? Why so glum?"

"It's a long, boring story and I'm sure you are far too busy to listen to my woes."

"On the contrary, I have all the time in the world." To Maximillion Crooked, any story the daughter of Emerson Hackerton had to tell was worth listening to.

"Well, I had another row with my sister, Astrid, when I met her for lunch today. She still thinks we should come clean about everything, but I agree with my parents. It would be a terrible career move for Daddy if the media found out about the family connection with the house. And then, of course, there is the money. Daddy says if it exists it is tainted, so he doesn't want anything to do with it. He worries that people will think he used it to further his campaign, if it were found."

In those few short moments, Max had no idea what Imogen's intoxicated words meant. Nevertheless, it only took one word to grab his attention. Money. It was a small word, but could be a most valuable one, and Max had a feeling it was going to be a good afternoon.

"I don't think I quite understand where the money is and why your father thinks it is tainted." Max was keen to find out as much as he could.

"Hacker Hall, of course."

"I'm afraid I don't know it. I'm not from Pennsylvania. I am just passing through on business, but I'd like to hear all about it, if it helps. Waiter, please get Miss Hackerton another drink."

"Hacker Hall was an asylum for the clinically insane over a hundred years ago. It was owned by Daddy's great-great-grandfather, Harrison Hacker. It is said that he did torturous things to the patients and extorted money from them and their rich families in order to pay for their keep. Our family are ashamed by what he did. We even changed our name to Hackerton in an attempt to keep the story hidden. Although Astrid does not agree. She thinks we should own up to who we are and live off the money, even if it means the end of Daddy's career."

"How much money are we talking about?"

"Oh, I don't know. Around twenty million dollars, I think."

"Twenty million! Wow, maybe your sister has a point. You could live quite nicely on that sort of money. Won't your parents listen to her?"

"Afraid not. Astrid is rather *persona non grata*. She had a baby when she was just seventeen, which my parents said disgraced the family name, so she decided to leave. My niece is called Frances and is twelve now."

"Yeah, yeah, less of the family history. What about the money? Does your family know where it is?"

"Apparently, it is hidden somewhere in the house. Of course, it is only a story passed down through our family, so I guess we will never know for sure. But that is okay. It is more important to keep a good family name."

"That is quite a story, Imogen. I think you've had enough to drink and it's getting late. How about I drive you home, and maybe tomorrow night I could take you to dinner?"

Max had dropped her home that afternoon and taken her to dinner the following evening. She felt comfortable with him and believed she could trust him. How wrong she had been.

"Okay, where to?" Imogen asked Max, as she turned up the heater in the rented car.

"The hotel. There is nothing more we can do today, so let's have some dinner and then sit tight until we hear from Muir."

"Sure, Max, anything you say – if it means we are a step nearer to this situation being over."

Max had booked himself and Imogen into a hotel in Brooklyn. It was cheaper than those near the television studio on the Upper East Side.

When they met for dinner in the bar later that evening, he had already received a call from Muir Mason.

"The advert is going out in tomorrow's editions of *USA Today*, *The New York Times*, the *Los Angeles Times*, *The Washington Post*, the *Chicago Tribune* and *The Boston Globe*. Hopefully then we can head back to Pennsylvania and wait for Muir to arrange a date to visit the hall," Max told Imogen, when the waiter escorted them to their table.

"Good, I don't like New York. It's too noisy and everyone is in such a hurry."

"Look, you are part of this plan, Imogen. You had to be here in case I needed back-up with Muir, but everything is working out nicely. If we keep our heads, it will be plain sailing and we can go our separate ways soon enough."

They spent a tense dinner together and Imogen was glad to get back to the peace and security of her hotel bedroom. As she waited to fall asleep, memories of that first dinner with Max entered her head. She knew she had drunk too much the afternoon before and he had been kind enough to drive her home, so agreeing to have dinner with him had been the least she could do. But looking back, regrettably, she wished she had never accepted.

"I am so glad we met, Imogen. I know I'm only passing through Pennsylvania, but I do feel that we were destined to meet," Max had told her. "You remember last night you told me about the house that your great-great-great-grandfather ran and the money he hid there. Well, Imogen, I have a plan and you are going to assist me with it."

"A plan? A plan for what?"

"A plan to get us into the house to find the money. And when it is found, I will relieve your family of it and disappear from your lives forever."

"You have to be kidding." Imogen almost choked on her bread roll. "We don't even know if the money is real. And if it is, what makes you think I will help you find it?"

"My dear Imogen, for the simple reason that if you don't, the whole world will know who Daddy's great-great-grandfather was and what he did. And we must protect the family name above all else, mustn't we?"

"It seems you are a vile, despicable man, Maximillion Crooked." Imogen was stunned at this sudden turn of events. "God, and to think I rather liked you. Would you really stoop that low?" Imogen was disgusted at what Max had suggested, although she knew she had no alternative. Her good family name was vital for her father's career and she would do anything to keep it that way, even if it meant helping Max carry out his plan.

"You have no idea how low one would stoop for twenty million dollars. The plan is perfect. We won't even have to do the searching ourselves. And maybe, if we are successful, I might even give you a cut for your trouble."

"It may be my family's money, Max, but if it is found, I don't want anything to do with it – the same as my father. You are welcome to it. Please just keep our family out of it."

"Excellent decision, Imogen. Let's get this plan underway. I hope your diary is clear. We are off to New York."

"Whatever you say, Max."

And there they were, having put the plan forward to the television network. The idea was a sound one and would make for a very entertaining TV show. Max had done the hard work so far and the network seemed to be on board. As Imogen fell asleep, she hoped she could return home to Pennsylvania soon. The sooner everything was arranged, the sooner they could get on with live show and the sooner Max would have the money and be out of her life for good.

The next morning, the phone rang early in Max's hotel room, which woke him from his slumber in the enormous queen-sized bed. Muir Mason had been in contact with the legal team at the network and the programme had been given the go-ahead.

"Everything is set, Max. We have the okay to move ahead as soon as possible. I don't need your assistance here in New York any further, so if you want to head back to Pennsylvania, I will be in touch soon, when I can join you there for a tour of the house."

"And what about the advert and choosing the applicants?" Max enquired.

"As promised, I got straight onto the advert as soon as you left yesterday. It will be appearing in the newspapers we talked about, in both the early and late editions. I will have my assistant run through the applicants' letters as they come in and whittle them down. She will find the children she thinks have possibilities. I will then cut them down to a final ten and when I meet you in Pennsylvania, we can sit down and decide on the final five. How does that sound?"

"It sounds exciting, Muir. I can't thank you enough for making this happen. I have a really good feeling about it." In reality, the only thing Max was excited about was getting his hands on twenty million dollars.

Maximillion Crooked was exactly as his name suggested. At thirty-five years of age, thus far his life had amounted to nothing. His school career began by bullying his classmates out of their lunch money and ended when he was expelled for robbing the cafeteria. He had never been married but he had been engaged six times, extorting money from the women before leaving them at the altar.

For the last ten years, he had travelled around the United States, dodging and dealing anything and everything illegal he could find. Waiting for the one get-rich scheme he had always known was out there. And now, at last, he had found it.

"Oh, me too, Max. Me too. And that feeling you have is because it's going to be a hit TV show. I am so glad you brought the idea to me. Now, safe journey back and I will call you in a few days."

Max and Imogen arrived at New York Penn Station and were waiting to board the Amtrak train that would take them the one hundred and ninety miles back to Pennsylvania when Max purchased the morning copy of *The New York Times*. On page five, he saw the advert.

"Look, Imogen, the advert! Just as Muir promised it would be." Max handed her the paper to read.

New York TV Network Calls Fearless 12 to 18-Year-Olds Seeking Fun, Fear and Finance

If you would like the chance to take part in a spookily special TV show with the possibility of winning $100,000, send an application, detailing your name, age and contact details. Tell us something special about yourself, where you live and what your hobbies are. You must be able to travel to New York and Pennsylvania within the next two months, and confident enough to enter an ancient, derelict building to search out the prize money.

ONLY THE BRAVE NEED APPLY
MMNYTV, P O Box 4321, NY 10101-8765 US

"I guess this thing is actually going to happen then," she said as she handed the paper back.

At least he thought that's what she said. Her voice was drowned out by the noise of the train pulling into the station.

"Oh yes, Imogen. It is happening, most definitely. And I am so glad to have you along for the ride."

Two

COMPETITION LAUNCH

A week later, the television network had received almost fifteen thousand entries for the competition. Muir Mason was delighted. He knew that the huge numbers brought in by the publicity of the advert meant that far greater numbers would follow when the show was aired.

Muir had cleared his diary in order to head off to Pennsylvania the following week and was keen to get the applications cut down to the last ten before he left. He had been busy filming his latest sitcom and had not had time to give a lot of thought to Max's show, but once he and his crew arrived in Pennsylvania everything would be different. Max and the show would have his full attention.

"How is carving up the applications going?" Muir asked his assistant, at the end of a long day's filming.

"Very well, Mr Mason. It has been rather easier than expected. Mostly the applications are nonsense or not overly exciting. It is getting harder the fewer I have left, but I am confident I will have it down to ten by the time you leave."

"Excellent, Carol. How many have you got it down to so far?"

"I have about twenty-five left and they are all very good applications."

"Well, I have some time now. If you don't mind leaving the remaining ones on my desk. You head off for the evening and I will take a look at them."

"Very good, Mr Mason. Goodnight then."

Muir Mason settled down, alone in his office, after every member of the crew had left. He sat and studied what was left of the applications for some time. Carol, his assistant, had been right. It was not as difficult a task as he had anticipated. He looked at photographs and read each entry.

The first one to spark his attention was Zach Hamilton. A seventeen-year-old from Pennsylvania. Muir's initial thought was that a local boy was a good idea to show support for the community. His photo showed a strapping, handsome young lad and his profile said he had high hopes to major in tennis at the University of Southern California. He wrote that he lived with his overprotective mum and three dogs. Sadly, his father had died when he was six years old. He had attended the primary school in Hackers Hollow and, every day, would walk past a ghostly old building called Hacker Hall, which he hoped very much was where the show might take place. As a young boy, he and his friends were always warned never to go near it and definitely never to go in. When he was seven, he was dared to enter the house, whilst playing a truth or dare game. He knew he would be teased and called a coward if he did not, but in reality he lacked the courage. Consequently, he told his friends he would not disobey his mother when she was in such a fragile state after his father's death. He was, of course, called a coward, and before long the incident was forgotten. Zach, however, never forgot.

And now, ten years later, if he could enter the house, it would be the last chance he would have before heading to university to put the record straight and prove, once and for all, he was no coward.

Muir Mason found the whole story a sad one and loved the sentimentality of it. This boy had been through the loss of a parent at such a young age. He had also held onto the idea that he, in some way, needed to prove himself to his peers, even now – ten years later. Muir knew instantly that he wanted Zach for his show. He could restore this young man's faith in himself and show the world he was no coward, leaving the boy with a tremendously proud mother when he left for college a year later. Yes, Zach Hamilton was perfect. The first candidate had been found.

The next letter that grabbed his attention was from a thirteen-year-old called Breena Mathis. From her picture, Muir could see she was a girl of mixed race, and she lived in Florida with her grandmother. There was no mention of her parents and Muir wondered what sort of circumstance would lead to a young teenager living with a grandparent. He studied the photograph she had sent of herself and thought her one of the most beautiful young women he had ever seen. Her brilliant blue eyes stood out against her sun-kissed skin and shining, long black hair. She abruptly wrote of her disappointment in the television network, due to the fact that they had chosen not to publish a notice of the competition in any Floridian newspaper and how fortuitous it had been for her that she happened to be visiting her aunt in Boston and came across the advert by chance.

Muir smiled at her words and felt that he had been duly ticked off. If it was her way of making the competition organisers take notice, it had worked. Breena ended her profile detailing how she loved to watch horror films and read scary novels. She closed by saying her dream was to be a presenter of a ghost-hunting show when she finished her education and believed entering the house would be the perfect way to kick-start her future career.

It was a well-presented and beautifully written letter, and Muir was certain that Breena was going to be one of his final five. He had not met this young woman yet, but already knew he would like her and looked forward to having her on the show.

Muir looked through several more applications before he settled on an envelope with the initials 'JFLA' stamped in large red letters in the top left-hand corner. He recognised it instantly as the largest television network in California and wondered about its contents. Inside, he found a short and direct letter from fourteen-year-old Henry Fortune. Muir knew instantly he was the son and heir of Johnson Fortune, head and owner of the network. They lived in a large house in central Beverly Hills and had a beach house on the coast in Malibu.

The letter got straight to the point, with Henry saying that it would be in the best interest of the New York studio to allow him to take part in the show. It had already been arranged that he could take time off from his expensive private school, and that if they did not take him, his father could use his money and his power to make life very difficult for the smaller, East Coast network.

There was no photograph with the application, but Muir could tell the sort of young man Henry was. The letter gave Muir a strong indication that he already had a dislike for this boy. He sounded as if he were a complete spoilt brat, with little or no respect for anyone or anything, and believed that he could have whatever he wanted, when he wanted it. He seemed like the last child Muir would have chosen for the show and agreeing to have Henry on board went against the grain of everything he stood for. Unfortunately, though, if he ignored or rejected the application, the power that Johnson Fortune held could make Muir's life exceedingly difficult. So, for the sake of the network, Muir knew he had no choice other than to give Henry one of the five places.

The telephone in Muir's office rang a short time later and he looked up briefly to see that two hours had passed since his assistant had gone home for the evening.

"I was wondering if you will be home in time for dinner, Mr Mason?" He recognised the voice of his housekeeper straightaway. Still a bachelor at forty-six, Muir had given his life to his career and the network, and greatly valued the care she took of him. He would never have dared to admit it, but he would have been lost without her.

"No, I don't think I will. I still have some finishing up here at, the studio. I will grab something on the way home. You run along home and I will see you in the morning."

"Very good, Mr Mason. Good evening."

He replaced the receiver, determined to continue finding competitors until he had all five. With three down and only two to go, he was over halfway there.

He flicked through another half a dozen applications, until an envelope written in a beautiful calligraphy-style script caught his eye. Inside was an equally beautiful letter. Almost a work of art. Neat and meticulous in every way; Muir wondered if the applicant would be the same.

Cait Luu was sixteen and had moved to New York two years before. She had come, with her parents, from Hong Kong in order to attend The New York Performing Arts Academy on a scholarship she had been awarded.

As a young girl, Cait had shown incredible promise as a ballet dancer. She had been noticed by a talent scout when she gave a magnificent performance as the Black Swan from *Swan Lake* in her local theatre. They had seen huge ability and paid for her trip to New York to audition for the academy. Six months later, she was on her way. Her only regret was that her grandparents were unable to join them in their new life and she dearly hoped that one day she would make enough money to bring them to New York.

Cait explained in the letter that she had two ways of doing just that – and both ways led to the hall. The first was to dance her way to fame. She had the potential to be an outstanding ballet dancer but lacked self-assurance. Her madame declared, on many occasions, that she must find a way to lose her fears in order to boost her confidence and become a 'complete' dancer. Cait believed that entering the house would allow her to confront her fears and be rid of them forever. The second, and a much simpler option, was to enter the house and win the money.

Muir grinned to himself and thought how intelligent this young lady had been to come up with such a concept. Her application was neat and clever, and something about her made Muir realise it was not just a tall tale to guarantee her a place, but that it was all true. Muir Mason had found his fourth contestant and he could not have been more delighted.

It was extremely late by the time Muir had sifted through twenty-four of the applications. One application left and one last competitor to find. He was tired and hungry and hoped that his assistant had been accurate in her choice of finalists. And if she was, then the last letter he had to open would fill the final place.

The letter was from a twelve-year-old girl called Frankie Hatter. Again, it was a short letter and gave little information about her personal life, other than a belief her family were in some way connected to a house called Hacker Hall – where she guessed the show may be filmed – although she did not know how. She, too, was from Pennsylvania and claimed to have been in the hall when she was small. Apparently, she was told it was haunted and gave an accurate report, identical in detail to the photographs Muir had seen, of what the house was like on the inside. Her plea was to go into the house and prove it was not haunted, then maybe her family could settle their differences once and for all.

She sounded like a charming girl, who was concerned about some sort of family politics and wanted to play her part in trying to help her family reconnect. It was a sweet gesture and Muir thought that if he had ever had a daughter, he would have liked her to be like Frankie. She was the second entrant to have correctly predicted the venue of the show and, at the end of the day, it may prove useful to the other contestants to have someone around that had been in the house before. His assistant had picked wisely. It had been a long evening, but Muir Mason had his final five.

Before he left the studio that night, Muir quickly composed an email to his assistant, asking her to make reservations at the Hackers Hollow Guesthouse for himself, Max Crooked and his associate, and the crew of eight from the studio one week ahead. He expected they could be there for up to a week and left instructions that they would require exclusive use of the guesthouse, and he would pay double for the privilege if need be.

He stopped to purchase a single helping of Chinese food on his walk home and, once in the privacy of his Madison Avenue apartment, picked up the telephone.

"Max, Muir here. Sorry it's rather later. It's been a long day. How's life in my second favourite state?"

"Muir, hi. It's good to hear from you. All good at this end. How are things progressing with our plans?"

"Things are moving along nicely. I have left instructions for reservations to be made at the Hackers Hollow Guesthouse for all of us. Are you and your associate able to meet us there next Thursday?" Muir assumed that as they had a deadline with the live show, the date would not be too soon.

"Yes, most definitely. I am a free agent at the moment and I am certain that Miss Hackerton will be available." Max knew he had Imogen in his hands, so she would drop everything if he told her to.

"Excellent. I don't know where you are currently staying and I know Miss Hackerton is local, but I think it makes sense for us all to be in one place. We can bounce ideas and strategies off each other if we are all under the same roof."

"Fine by me, Boss. Just say the word and I am there."

"I also have good news regarding the contestants. I had my assistant vet the applications, and having gone through the final twenty-five, I have set upon five that I believe will be simply perfect. Of course, I will show you their applications. I want you to be happy with the ones we settle on. It is your show, after all. I had expected to only get the list down to ten by now, but it was a relatively easy decision. I think you will be extremely satisfied with the five I have chosen."

"That's okay with me, Muir. You're the experienced one in these matters. I've never made a TV show before, remember. I will gladly take a look at them, but I am happy to trust your judgment at the end of the day."

As it stood, Max did not really care about who was chosen to enter the house. How different could children be? As far as he was concerned, any five would do, as long as one of them found the money and handed it over to him at the end of the show.

"Good, that's everything settled then. In the meantime, if you and Miss Hackerton have any ideas for the camera work and graphics, make a call through to the special effects team and have a chat. They are already working on some suggestions I put forward. I would also like you and Miss Hackerton to have as much input as possible, and the more information they have before we come to Pennsylvania, the more prepared they can be."

"Sure, we will put our heads together and see what we can come up with."

"Right you are then, Max. We are hoping to get to Hackers Hollow in the late afternoon, so maybe we can all get together for a dinner meeting. How does that sound?"

"Sounds perfect, Muir. We will see you next Thursday. And once again, thanks for making this happen."

"My pleasure, Max. As I told you before, I believe we can make a great team. See you next week."

Muir replaced the receiver, finished eating his takeaway dinner, took a shower and climbed into bed. The last few days had been more hectic than normal and for the first time in months, he did not set his alarm. The next few weeks were going to take on a new direction, working outside the studio, and Muir elected to have a late start the following morning. He was the boss and if he wanted to sleep late on a rare occasion, he could.

"Imogen, Muir called last night. Things are moving along nicely." Max telephoned his 'friend' early the next morning.

"Good morning to you, too. How nice to hear from you at such an ungodly hour. Ready to brighten my day?" Imogen was sleepy and did not relish being woken up.

"Yes, yes. Sarcasm does not become you. This TV show is going ahead six weeks from now, so you had better get on board. You know what is at stake and you ought to be a little nicer to me under the circumstances."

"Look, Max, I am going along with this because you left me no choice, but I will never be happy about it. And we are not friends or pals or anything else, for that matter. I will do what is necessary to keep you onside, but no more. Now, was there a reason you called so early?"

"Ah yes, listening to your charming, early-morning, dulcet tones, I almost forgot. Muir and the crew from the network will be arriving next Thursday. They are checking into the Hackers Hollow Guesthouse and they have made reservations for the both of us."

"I hope you told him to book separate rooms for us. I don't want him thinking we are an item or anything," Imogen stressed.

"Really, old girl. You don't fancy sharing a room with Maxi?"

"Don't tease, Max. We share a room over my dead body."

"Careful what you say, my lovely, bearing in mind why we are going to Hackers Hollow."

"I don't see why I can't stay at home and drive over to the hall when I am needed."

"Oh no. You are as much a part of this plan as I am. Muir wants us both on hand so we can add our input and ideas. You, of course, know the house – my one quick visit was not substantial enough to know the place inside out. So, if he wants to pay to put us both up, I, for one, am not going to complain."

"There you go again, Max. Is there anything in your life that is not about the money?"

"My dear Imogen, you know me so well in such a short space of time. I knew there was a reason you entered my life. Now, just clear that social-climbing calendar of yours and I will pick you up next Thursday at three. And don't forget to tell Mummy and Daddy you will be away for a few days."

"Oh, Max, you are such a charmer. No wonder you never married. Those women don't know what lucky escapes they had. I will see you next week."

"Charming old Max, that's me. Now, go back to sleep or do whatever your day holds for you. Bye for now, Imogen."

THREE

A TRIP TO
HACKERS HOLLOW

The following Thursday, five weeks before the show was due to be aired, Muir Mason and his crew drove in three cars – three men in each with a multitude of equipment from cameras, computers, generators and boom mics. They travelled two hundred and twenty miles, due west out of New York, towards Hackers Hollow. Once through Williamsport, their drive took them northwest. The terrain became more rural and remote, and towns were few. The route included scenery of rocky ridges and waterfalls with clear, fast flowing streams, and in the distance stood a magnificent view of the Appalachian Mountains, covered by a forest of greenery as far as the eye could see.

The team communicated with each other between the three vehicles and were beginning to feel as though their sat-nav systems had let them down. It had been a long drive and they were all keen to reach their destination and relax before they got stuck into their mission.

The lead car eventually saw a small, brown road sign indicating that Hackers Hollow was three miles ahead. They continued straight and, sure enough, ten minutes later, the caravan of three cars pulled into the town of Hackers Hollow (population: four thousand, two hundred).

The small remote town seemed to consist of a main central street with a store, a bookshop, a hair salon, a bank and a bar. And finally, beyond them all, the Hackers Hollow Guesthouse.

Muir and his crew unpacked the equipment, fearful of leaving it in the vehicles, and on signing in, inquired as to whether Mr Crooked and Miss Hackerton had checked in. The guesthouse proprietor told Muir they had arrived together and had taken to their rooms. Muir sent word to both their rooms to have them meet him in the bar at seven o'clock, giving them all time to get acquainted before they sat down for a wholesome country meal that the guesthouse had promised to lay on.

At five past seven, Imogen walked into the bar area of the quaint, country guesthouse. The ten men she would be spending the next few days with had already assembled. Imogen was unaware of how beautiful she was and the group all turned to stare as she approached them.

"Gentlemen, allow me to introduce Imogen Hackerton," Max said, escorting her to a chair.

"Good evening, everyone," Imogen said, as she took a seat.

"Imogen, this is Muir Mason."

"I'm pleased to meet you, Mr Mason," she said politely, shaking his hand.

"The pleasure is mine, my dear. Please call me Muir. This is Gil, our head production manager, and the rest of the crew. We are happy to have you on board," Muir said, as the rest of the team said hi, nodded or shook her hand.

Max passed her a glass of white wine, remembering she was rather partial, and Gil noticed that she seemed to wriggle uncomfortably in her chair, as if trying to move away from him. Nothing was said, but Gil made a mental note that all may not be well between the two. Gil was a first-class producer, and his knack for paying attention and spotting the tiniest detail made him so.

"So, Imogen," Muir spoke again, "I recognise your name. Any relation to Congressman Hackerton?"

"Yes, actually. He is my father," she said, proudly.

"You are a lucky young lady. I have not had the pleasure of meeting him, although I gather he is an immensely popular and well-thought-after man."

"Thank you. Yes, he is pretty amazing, but I am slightly biased. And it is his greatest ambition to become senator next year. He has worked awfully hard and deserves it," she said, throwing Max a hard stare.

Once again, Gil picked up on it. Yes, there was definitely something not quite right there. The rest of the group chatted happily, getting to know each other, and at a quarter to eight, the guesthouse owner asked them to head into the dining room for dinner.

Imogen steered clear of Max as they entered and sat comfortably between Muir and Gil at the centre of the long table. The chatting and drinking continued until after the meal when Muir asked Imogen what she knew of Hacker Hall.

"Being a local girl, I have known about it all my life. It is sort of fixed in the folklore of the area. Many tales have been told about it over the years," she said, making sure she gave nothing away of her family connection.

"What is so special about the place, that it has gained such notoriety?" Muir wanted to know everything.

"Way back in 1870, a man called Harrison Hacker settled in the town. He was well liked and immensely popular, and within a few years, aged just thirty, was voted in as the youngest mayor the town had ever known. He made a good living and with his savings bought the house we know today as Hacker Hall. He carried out extensive repairs on the house, being one of the first to install coils to heat the water and gas lamps to replace the candles and oil lamps. And when ready, he opened the doors of Hacker Hall, Home for the Insane and Destitute.

At first, the townspeople thought it a wonderful, caring place where patients could go to get well and improve their lives. Everyone in the town was so proud of Harrison that they even changed the name of the town to Hackers Hollow. Before long, Harrison realised there was a vast amount of money to be made. Patients began to enter the house and never leave. Soon, he became nicknamed 'Hacker the Horrible'. He took in patients of rich families who wanted to be rid of a relative to inherit their money, or husbands that wanted rid of a wife that was 'in the way'. Those people paid a high price to have their loved ones committed."

"My God! Did no one try to do anything about it?"

"Well, he got away with it as he used the word 'destitute' in the name. It made him look caring – that he would take in anyone who needed his help. In reality, that was not the case. If you had no money, you didn't get through the door. Those that did get through the door had to have money – and plenty of it. Inmates that checked-in of their own accord, preferably with no family, were offered a permanent home for a large fee. It only required the signatures of two doctors to say a person was insane and that was that. They were legally committed and if they were reluctant to pay up, Hacker found a way to make sure they did."

"I saw some of the photographs that Max took when he visited the place with you. They all looked pretty gruesome. Can I ask how you were able to visit the hall? Surely it is not open to the public."

"Let's just say, it helps to have a father who is a congressman."

"I understand. People in high places can be especially useful sometimes. Do you know what happened to Hacker and why the hall closed?" asked Muir.

"The story goes that an inmate called Elizabeth Brute was subjected to many years of electroshock treatment for her headaches. Apparently, still sane enough to know what she was doing, she soaked Hacker from head to toe in water and inflicted the electroshock probes on him. His charred body was later found by one of the doctors."

"Sounds horrific," Gil commented, having listened to the macabre story Imogen had told.

"Many said he got his 'just deserts'. A terrible way to die, nonetheless," Imogen said, with mixed feelings. Harrison Hacker had done awful things, but he was still her great-great-great-grandfather, after all.

"So, Boss, what time are we heading over to the house from hell tomorrow?" Gil asked.

"Oh yes, nearly forgot with all the excitement of your storytelling, Imogen. We are meeting the town councillor at the hall tomorrow morning at eight-thirty, so it's an early start, I'm afraid. We just have to sign a couple of forms for him and we are in, so I suggest we call it quits for the night. Let's meet in the foyer, ready to leave at eight o'clock. Goodnight, everyone. Sleep well."

Everyone left the dining room and made their way to their bedrooms, and as Imogen reached her door, Max caught up with her.

"A good story you told tonight at dinner. I did wonder, for a second there, if you might let something slip."

"Give me some credit, Max. I know how this has to go and I will not do anything to jeopardise things. Now, if there's nothing else, I will see you in the morning."

"Sure, Imogen. Sleep tight, it's a big day tomorrow," Max replied, as he walked along the hallway to his own room. He did not, however, see Gil standing in the shadows of a nearby alcove.

The next morning, the guesthouse owner had laid out a buffet-style breakfast. The crew were all up and ready to leave, and quickly grabbed some croissants and fresh fruit to eat on the way. The drive to the hall only took ten minutes out of town towards the forest, and Imogen went in a car with Gil and Muir, who was driving.

"Everything all right with you and Max?" Gil asked, as their car left the town.

"Sure. Why?" Imogen thought it was an odd thing to ask, as she had only met him the evening before.

"Probably my imagination. Thought I picked up on a strange vibe between the two of you, that's all. My mistake, I guess—"

"Yes, you must be mistaken, Gil. Max is one of the good ones. Right, Imogen?" Muir interrupted their conversation.

"Right, Muir," Imogen replied. "Oh Gil, I have been meaning to ask you about your name. Is Gil short for something?" She wanted to change the subject away from her relationship with Max.

"Sure is. My name is actually 'Ferdinand Gillespie'. Go on, it's okay to laugh."

"I wouldn't dream of it."

"Well, I hate Ferdinand, as you can imagine. And when I was small, I could not pronounce 'Gillespie', so it became 'Gil' and it has been ever since."

"I think 'Gil' is just fine," Imogen smiled, feeling a warmth towards him. "Look, guys. There it is. Straight ahead."

"Looks like the gates are still locked. We will have to wait for the chap from the council so we can gain entry. He should be here any second," Muir said.

Muir parked the car and the other two cars pulled up behind immediately after. The group of eleven left their cars and slowly walked to the gates. They were covered with ivy interwoven between the rusty old bars. The hinges looked rotten, too, and it was a wonder the gates were still standing after a hundred years. The house could not be seen as the drive curved behind a group of dense trees. Imogen explained that the drive was long to ensure better seclusion from the road.

A black car pulled up a moment later and a small, mousey-looking man emerged. He explained that he was from the council offices in Williamsport and that the council had full jurisdiction over the house, while the owners contemplated what to do with the place. Muir asked who the owners were and Imogen breathed a sigh of relief when the councillor said he was not at liberty to say. He also informed them that all dealings with the hall must be dealt with through his office.

Muir signed a release form, a non-disclaimer and an insurance form, and the paperwork was done. The councillor unlocked the padlock, removed the chain and handed over the keys. While he asked Muir to make sure the property was secure every time they left and to return the keys to him at his office in Williamsport when they were finished, Gil and Max slowly pushed open the creaking, rusty gates.

The councillor wished the crew the best of luck with their production, climbed into his car and vanished back along the lane. The group got back into their cars and made the short journey along the entrance driveway and parked up in front of the hall.

Muir, Imogen and Gil were the first to leave their vehicle and all three stared at the Gothic-style monster that stood before them. They were quickly joined by the rest of their party and the silence that spread over the area had a spooky eeriness. All eleven stood looking up at the grey brick building with arched stone mullion windows covered in iron bars, which they knew were to prevent escapees. There were three visible floors. The attic rooms rested within the eaves of the roof and Imogen explained that there was also a basement below ground, making four floors in all. At a quick calculation, the building had fourteen windows from left to right and was accessed via a large wooden veranda that led to a double-fronted, arched pair of solid oak doors. There were several pointed apexes to the roof, and a spectacular, tall, round turret, surrounded by grotesque-looking gargoyles, topped the centre of the building.

The condition of the house was less than desirable with most of the paint peeled off the veranda. Many of the wooden newel posts were missing and the handrail was broken in many places. The brickwork of the house was intact, although dirty, while most of the windows contained shattered or no glass at all.

It was a building stuck in a time warp of gruesome history and was probably the most haunting building the group had ever seen. It had an ominous air of sadness, foreboding and even death. And where the turret met the sky, a ghastly grey mist loomed overhead.

"It's a real charmer, isn't it?" Max broke the silence. "What do you reckon, guys, are you ready to head inside?"

"You bet we are." Muir wanted to show his crew there was nothing to worry about. "Let's get this show on the road."

He led the way onto the veranda and as he stepped forward from the top step, the wooden slats underfoot gave way and his left leg disappeared through a rotten plank.

"Careful there, Boss." Gil darted forward and grabbed hold of Muir's arm to steady him, so he could free his limb.

"Great start – and we are not even in yet!" Muir joked, as he moved forward and unlocked the front door with the keys the councillor had given him.

"That is the least of it," Max said, stepping forward over the newly made hole. "You have to keep your eyes open inside." He followed Muir in.

Gil waited and held out his hand to help Imogen carefully over the hole, then followed her inside, along with the rest of the crew.

The main foyer was a large, almost octagonal-shaped area with five doors leading off it. There was no furniture, just a series of antique bells high on one of the walls, each with a rope bell pull below.

"God, what is that awful smell?" one of the crew members said, holding his nose.

"I don't think anyone got the air freshener out or cleaned up for our arrival," Max joked. "I promise you; this is nothing. It will get way worse than this."

"Okay, I guess it is up to Max and Imogen from here," Muir said. "You have both been here before. Any ideas where we should start?"

"We should head through the door to your left. If I remember correctly, it is some sort of office. Maybe we can get our bearings," Imogen said, knowing the house better than any of them.

"Good idea. Gil, you and the boys unload the cars and bring the gear into the office. Max, Imogen and I will wait for you."

"Will do, Boss."

The eight-man crew exited the front door once again, careful not to fall foul of the broken veranda. Muir, Imogen and Max moved through the first door into another peculiar-shaped room. It was a gloomy, stark room that housed the remains of an old desk, two broken chairs and a bookcase, whose shelves had fallen and left the tattered remainder of books scattered all over the floor.

"Right, Imogen, it's definitely an office. Where to from here?" Muir asked.

"I'm not sure how much Max told you. The house consists of dozens of rooms. Most of the rooms interconnect with very few corridors, which is what made the house especially unusual. Just doors from one room leading straight into the next."

"Ah, Max, that is why you called it the 'House of a Hundred Doors'. Good. I like that. Do you know how many rooms it actually has?"

"I'm not sure anyone has ever counted. Moving around, you will see there are an awful lot. I would guess at around sixty or seventy," Imogen answered.

"Interesting. Please carry on with your description," Muir said.

"Well, the basement housed the morgue and was used for treatments, experiments and, unfortunately, torture. There is also an area of several secure cells down there where they kept the most violent and disobedient patients. The attic is much smaller than the other floors, due to the shape of the eaves. It housed rooms for the staff to live in. There is also a large, open storage area up there. Then, the two floors between contain kitchens, several lounge rooms, a dining hall, a couple of offices, a library, shower blocks and dormitories. Lastly, a private wing on the second floor is where Hacker and his two senior doctors had their personal rooms."

"It certainly is a huge and most unusual place, as you say. Perfect for our show, wouldn't you say, Max?"

"Sure is, Muir. I knew you would love it." Max tried hard to contain the thrill of being back at the hall – for it meant his show was well underway and he was one step closer to the money.

"How long did Hacker own the place for, Imogen?" Muir asked, as the rest of the crew entered the room and placed down their mountains of equipment.

"It opened in 1876 and closed in 1913, shortly after Hacker was found dead. He ruled this terrible place for thirty-seven years, having had a free reign to perform terrible atrocities and behave exactly as he pleased. I do wonder how much longer it would have gone on for if he had not been killed."

"Well, no need to worry about that now, dear lady. Hacker is long gone and we have work to do. I think the first thing we need is a map of the place. Let's see if we can lay down some graphics, so we know which way we are coming and going. We have a fairly good idea of the basement and the attic from what Imogen has told us. So, let's start putting together a picture of the two floors in between. Okay, everyone, let's explore."

The group left the office through a different door and found themselves in what looked like a medicine room of some kind. Large wooden cases with cracked glass doors hung on the walls and still contained dozens upon dozens of bottles. There were also a couple of white, metal, bureau-style cabinets on wheels, which must have been used to move medicines around the hall. A layer of settled dust and cobwebs covered every surface and spiders, actively making new homes, filled every crevasse.

The next door took them into a bare, white-tiled shower block, where – even though many of the tiles were smashed and scattered across the floor – it was clear for all to see that there would have been no privacy at all.

From there, another door took them into a dormitory-style bedroom where rows of beds filled the space. Some were made up with blackened sheets and torn blankets, while others had bare mattresses, stained with blood and bodily fluids. The one thing the beds had in common, though, were the bars on each side. As with the study, the walls were grey and the same, ghastly odour lingered throughout.

With the group making notes on the layout as they moved around, there was a strange silence between them as they took in their surroundings. The next door took them through a small linen store, with shelf upon shelf of folded blankets, towels and sheets. None of which looked particularly clean or sterile. Everyone could see that cleanliness had not been top of the agenda at the hall.

One more door took them into the largest room so far. It looked as though it may have been quite a glamorous room in its day and was the only room so far to show any colour. The walls were decorated with wallpapered panels and large mirrors, many of which were broken, and the floor, the first to have carpet.

"I remember this room," Imogen said. "It was used as a dining hall most of the time." She pointed to rows of stacked tables and chairs in one corner. "Although, once a year, they held some sort of open day. They let the public in to be wined and dined, and to see any inmate relations, if they wished. Most likely a publicity stunt."

"How did they manage that without the patients going wild?" Muir asked.

"Story goes that the patients were heavily drugged or sedated most of the time, so it would have been rare for any to misbehave. Those coherent enough also knew they would suffer terrible punishment if they were disobedient."

"My God. That's awful. Poor people," Gil commented. "Tell us, Imogen, how did you get to know so much about the hall?"

"Oh, mostly from books and articles. And, of course, stories that were told over generations and handed down. Most people in town know the stories. You can ask practically anyone and they know as much as I do."

As she spoke, Max smiled at her answer and wondered how close Imogen was to admitting the stories were handed down by her own family members. He knew she was being extra careful and he was becoming more confident she would not let anything slip. Gil, however, wondered what it was that had made Max smile.

Next, they entered a lounge area, with several wing-backed armchairs and a couple of sofas. The cushions, like the mattresses, were stained, and had springs and stuffing poking out through holes and tears in the fabric. The smell was even more putrid than earlier. Pungent, with the faint air of old body odour and urine. The group were keen to move on.

Within an hour, they had moved through a maze of at least half a dozen rooms, and it quickly become evident that there was no pattern or continuity to the layout of the rooms.

"This place is a proverbial bewilderment," one of the crew observed.

"Yeah, and I can see that the lack of structure here would have caused the patients to become stressed and anxious at not being able to find their way around. It is so confusing," Muir said.

"It was believed that moving directly from one room to another, with no order – say, bathroom to lounge – kept the patients in a state of confusion. It also prevented them from having any privacy, as rooms could be accessed from different sides, so there was always an element of surprise. Rather cruel, I have always thought. It must have upset them terribly," Imogen told the group.

"And you could bet they were punished, if they got lost or went where they shouldn't have," Max added.

"What a terrible state of affairs. Can you imagine ever putting a loved one or family member in a place like this? Thank God institutions like this don't exist anymore," Muir said.

"Here, here! Come on, let's move on," Gil added.

The next door took the group into a stairwell that led both up and down. They chose to go up first, fearing that once they went down and witnessed the basement, they may well want to vacate the house for a while to recover. So, up it was.

The first floor definitely seemed less confusing. Once out of the stairwell, a long straight corridor seemed to run the length of the building. Imogen had been right, in that there were private quarters for Hacker and his two senior doctors. Hacker had a bedroom and a bathroom, secluded in the corner of the floor, tucked away beyond a doctor's lounge. The other doctors also had private rooms and bathrooms, on either side of the passageway. Each of the three suites were virtually intact. Nicely decorated and fully equipped with decent furniture and home comforts.

"Amazing how different this part of the house is. Hacker certainly didn't live in the same conditions as his patients," Muir commented, having looked around the pleasant and well-preserved rooms.

"With the money he was making, he could afford to live like a king," Max said, throwing Imogen a resentful stare.

She ignored his comment and quickly pressed forward along the corridor, while the rest of the group peeked inside another dormitory and another storage area.

"Seriously, Imogen, what is the deal between you and Crooked? I am getting some really bad vibes between the two of you." Gil caught up with her while the others lingered to make notes.

"Oh, it's nothing really, Gil, but it is sweet of you to be concerned. I just think he is so set on making this show he can't think about anything else, which I understand. It's just that being a local and having lived with the stories of this place, I feel for everyone that stayed here. I see them as real people. Max just sees them as a TV show." Once again, Imogen was selective with the truth and hoped it would satisfy Gil's curiosity.

"Well, if he gives you any trouble, you let me know."

"I will, Gil, and thanks."

"What are you two lovebirds up to?" Muir teased, as they all reached the end of the corridor.

"Just getting better acquainted with the lady," Gil said, as Imogen opened the next door.

"If I have my bearings correct, this is the last room on this side of the building. We should find another stairwell at the other side of this dormitory," she said.

As Imogen had predicted, another set of stairs led up and down. Yet again, the group chose to head upwards, knowing they were entering the attic and the top floor of the hall. They were met by an area, open and spacious. It was littered with wooden chests and boxes, and old broken pieces of furniture. It looked like a dumping ground for anything and everything that was no longer needed on the floors below. It was a narrower space than the previous two levels. One side was completely cut off at the angle of the roof line, and the front section varied in height according to the gables.

Once through the open space, the group entered another straight passageway that extended the whole length of the loft space. One side was a series of staff bedrooms, with every two linked by a shared Jack-and-Jill bathroom. The other side was space for storage, built into the slant of the roof. At the far end of the corridor, the group noticed there was no second staircase to head back down.

"Sorry, guys, I forgot the staircase at this end only went as far as the first floor. We will have to retrace our steps and return the way we came," Imogen told them.

"So, it looks like we have covered everything up here. Only the basement to go. Is that right, Imogen?" Muir asked.

"Sure is. I'm a little hungry, though. I wouldn't mind a bite to eat."

"I agree with Imogen," Max said. "We have been at this several hours now and it is well past lunchtime. Besides, I don't think any of us should face the basement on an empty stomach."

"Agreed. Let's head back to the cars and grab the lunches the guesthouse prepared for us. Then, we can tackle the basement," Muir told everyone, relieved at the prospect of getting out into the fresh air for a while.

With lunch out of the way, the group re-entered the hall and the office they had first found. With three floors already covered, the crew, with the exception of Gil, decided to stay put and begin laying down a computerised plan of the house. Max and Imogen had one last floor to show Muir and Gil.

Returning to the medicine room and then down the nearest flight of stairs, the smaller group were faced with a choice of two doors.

"Which one?" Muir asked.

"If you remember the photographs I showed you, there are some gruesome sights down here. The door to the right is the morgue. That might be a better place to start than the door on the left," Max said.

"What do you think, Imogen? Do you agree with Max?"

"Yes, Muir. Probably a good idea, then we can exit immediately after seeing the last couple of rooms."

"Okay then. Max, lead the way."

As promised, the right-hand door took the four of them into the morgue. A large room, with black walls and hard, stone-slabbed floors. One side of the room was set out with three body-length metal tables; behind them was a set of cupboards with various sets of medical tools on the counter tops. The other side was a full wall of twelve small metal doors, four across and three high.

"You know what those are, don't you, Muir?" Max said.

"Yes, Max, they are the cold mortuary cabinets that housed the dead bodies before they were taken to be buried."

"I am amazed that they needed so many," Imogen said, moving forward and opening one of the cabinet doors. "Too many dead bodies if you ask… ahh!" she screamed, jumping backwards into Gil's chest as a large, brown rat leapt from inside one of the coffin-sized cabinets.

"Are you all right, Imogen?" Gil supported her arm as she steadied herself.

"Yes, Gil, thank you. Sorry about that." She was embarrassed for crashing into him so hard. "Rotten thing gave me a terrible fright."

"Of course. It would have shocked anyone."

"Shall we move on?" Max interrupted the moment, not liking the way Gil had looked at Imogen.

Through yet another door, the group entered another long hallway. They were met by almost pitch-darkness and the most nauseating, frowsty smell. This area of the house had clearly never seen any fresh air or daylight. Thankfully, Gil carried a torch and on one side they saw a series of doors, each leading to a small, padded cell, accessed via a steel door with a viewing flap. On the other side were also cells, but this time, minute. Each about the size of a telephone box, with steel walls, offering no protection for an inhabitant. They offered no viewing flap and must have only allowed a patient to stand bolt upright for the entirety of the time they were within them.

Muir, Max, Imogen and Gil remained speechless as they moved further along the corridor and entered a large dungeon-style room. The floor was laden with straw and, from the walls, chains hung from large iron rings.

"Sorry, guys," Imogen said, as tears began to flow from her eyes. "The very same thing happened last time I came here. This really is the most depressing place on earth. Please feel free to look around, but I think I would like to head back upstairs, if you don't mind."

"Ah, Imogen, not really your sort of place, is it?" Max pretended to sound sympathetic. "You head back up and I will finish down here with Muir and Gil."

"No, you and Muir stay. I will escort Imogen back," Gil said, quickly.

"Sure, you two head off. Max and I will follow you up shortly. There can't be much more down here."

"Thanks, Muir. See you shortly," Imogen said, noting the look on Max's face, which told her he was not happy.

Gil handed Imogen a handkerchief as the pair headed back towards the stairs.

"I really am sorry, Gil. You must think I'm a complete twit. When I think of all the awful things that happened in this house, especially down here, it breaks my heart."

"It's not a problem, honestly. I can see why anyone would be upset. I knew the place would be gruesome, but it has taken me by surprise just how terrible it is. Come on, let's get out of here."

They made their way back up the stairs, but then picked the wrong door on the ground-floor landing.

"One wrong door and we end up in the shower. God, this place is maddening. Which door back to the office, Imogen, do you know?"

"Yes, I think this one on our right will be back to the medicine room and then the office."

"Good, I'm right behind... ouch! Christ! What the hell was that?" Gil cried.

"Are you all right, Gil? What happened?" Imogen spun around.

"I'm not sure. Something sharp hit me from behind." Gil turned to look into the empty space of the white tiled shower room.

"Gil, you're bleeding. Your neck."

"That's odd. It looks like a piece of broken tile," he said, placing his hand over the back of his neck and looking down at a jagged broken tile on the floor close to his feet. "Don't suppose I could take my handkerchief back, could I?"

"Sure."

As Gil used the cotton hanky to cover the cut, he and Imogen made their way through the medicine room and back to the safety of the office where the rest of the crew were working.

"Hey, Imogen and I are going to head outside for some fresh air. You were wise not to go down there – it's weird. Max and Muir are still down there, but they must be nearly finished. They should be up any minute, then we can call it quits for today," Gil told his crew.

Meanwhile, still in the basement, Max led Muir back along a different section of corridor. Through one more door, the two men entered a room that spoke, very clearly, for itself. The walls were dirty and stained, where once they would have been gleaming white. There were a couple of beds with lamps overhead and five leather straps on each. A pair for the ankles, a pair for the wrists and one for the forehead. There were racks on the walls full of tools, including knives, forceps, pliers, hammers and even an axe. Then, even worse, placed centrally against the back wall was a platform, upon which sat a high-backed wooden chair. Again, with leather straps for the hands and feet. Protruding from the top of the chair was a metal cap, attached to wires and linked to a generator behind the chair.

"Good Lord! You know what, Max, I thought, being a filmmaker, I had seen everything. But this, I never imagined… It's the stuff of horror movies."

"I know. Incredible, isn't it? Unfortunately, the next room is more of the same."

Once through the door, they were met by a similar room, with beds and various equipment but no electric chair. Now, the centrepiece was a large, freestanding copper bathtub. Not too unnerving, except for the dipper hoist with a chair attached at one end.

"After the last room, I didn't think this place could get any worse. No wonder it upsets Imogen so."

"You have no idea," Max said, under his breath.

"You know, the photos you showed me don't even begin to portray the horrors that must have occurred here. Come on, Max. Let's get back to the guesthouse. I've seen enough for one day."

Four

CONFRONTING THE PAST

*M*ost of the crew ate supper in their bedrooms that night, all too disturbed to make conversation. It had been an eye-opening day. A group of adult men that considered themselves brave and strong had been shocked to the core by the conditions that were once inflicted on innocent human beings at Hacker Hall.

Before it was time to turn in, Muir sat in the bar for a nightcap. He was soon joined by Max, who also needed something to settle his nerves before going to sleep.

"I have told the boys that we will stay here in the morning and go over today's findings. When we left them during the afternoon, they got well underway with a layout map of the house. Now that is done, we can begin to plan what little extras we are going to add to confuse our competitors and amuse our audience."

"I have made a few notes on that. Perhaps we can go over those tomorrow, too."

"Sure, Max. I also want you to take a look at the five finalists I have found and if you agree with my choices, I can contact my assistant and ask her to call them and give them the good news."

"Excellent, Muir. Another busy day ahead. I think I will drink the whiskey in my room. Goodnight."

"Goodnight, Max."

After a good night's sleep, everyone gathered in the guesthouse dining room for a breakfast meeting. Some of the crew had worked late into the evening and completed a computer-generated floor plan of the four levels of the house.

"How is your neck this morning, Gil?" Imogen asked.

"Fine, thanks – nothing that some antiseptic and a large band-aid couldn't cure. It's a bit tender but nothing to worry about."

"Good, I'm pleased."

"Yeah, what do you think happened? Max interrupted their conversation. "Rather odd, don't you think? Especially with no one else in the shower room."

"Not really sure. It looked as though a tile fell from the wall and my neck got in the way!" Gil joked.

"It didn't just fall, Gil; it flew across the room."

"And you didn't see anyone, Imogen?"

"No, Max, it was just the two of us."

"Maybe the place is haunted, after all."

"Come now, Max. You can't really think that?" Muir said. "There is no such thing as ghosts. Just clever souls like us, who make people believe they exist. Now, talking of making places look haunted, can we get down to planning? Max, what do you have in mind?"

"Well, Muir, the rat in the morgue was an easy one. We can have rats in many of the places that the kids will search. Doors can be spring-loaded to slam shut automatically. There are plenty of spiders in the place, we can utilise those, and add our own giant ones. Maybe even some strategically placed snakes. Everyone is terrified of snakes."

"Good. Nothing too complicated there. All easy to put together. Gil, what have you and the boys come up with?"

"Nothing so straightforward, I'm afraid. We know we can use the rooms as they are, but we thought about giving the audience more of an adventure."

"I'm not sure I understand, Gil."

"Well, we can't take the contestants outside, so we have decided to bring the outside in. Taking the contestants on wild excursions inside the hall."

"A great idea, but sounds like a tall order. Can it be done, Gil?" Max questioned.

"Of course it can be done. It won't be easy. We have only used such effects in the studio before now. We can do the preparation when we get back and move everything to the hall for the show. It will make for great suspense and will definitely get the audience and contestants trembling… if we can pull it off."

"But can you pull it off?"

"Have confidence, Muir. Of course we can."

"Fantastic, that's what I like to hear. Right then, Gil, why don't you and the team head back to the hall after lunch and start planning what you want to do in each room? And remember to incorporate Max's ideas, too. Max, how about we stay here and go over the contestant list? I would like to get that finalised."

"Fine. If I don't have to step back in the house until the night of the show, that will suit me."

"Good, that's settled. Imogen, do you have any plans?"

"I think I will leave you and Max to sort out the contestants, so if you don't need me here, I might pop home. Daddy always needs help at the campaign office. I will be back in time for dinner."

"Not a problem; have a good day."

Gil and his team left in two cars, leaving one at the guesthouse in case Muir or Max needed it. Imogen called a taxi to take her the fifteen-minute journey back to her father's office.

In the early afternoon, Muir and Max met in the guesthouse lounge.

"I've ordered some coffee," Muir told Max as he sat down on the slightly worn sofa. "I have here the letters we received from the five entrants I like. We received nearly fifteen thousand in all. The advert far exceeded anything I had expected. All good publicity, though. You can bet your bottom dollar that the applicants that haven't been chosen will be watching with interest on the night. Some of them may even be the ones that purchase tickets for the live audience. Well, as you know, I had my assistant whittle them down and I have the other final twenty in my briefcase, if you are not happy with any of these five."

Muir placed the five letters on the coffee table, next to the tray of coffee that had just arrived. Max picked one up. He removed the letter from the already opened envelope and read for a few seconds. He really wasn't too bothered about looking at the applications, but he had to play the game. For the sake of his programme, he had to look interested.

"This girl, Cait Luu – it's the most perfect handwriting I have ever seen. A ballet dancer, eh? Definitely an arty type. Seems like she may be a bit flaky. Do we really want a scaredy-cat in there? Don't want the poor girl having a heart attack or anything."

"That was my first reaction. It was what she said about wanting to bring her grandparents from Hong Kong and the two options she gave to fulfil her plan that won me over. Very brave and very clever, I thought."

"Yes, you're right. I like her reasons, too. Yep, Cait is in."

"You may not be so confident with the next one." Muir had seen which envelope Max had picked up.

"Henry Fortune, really. Sounds like an absolute horror," Max said, after reading Henry's entrance letter.

"I know. He was the one I had my doubts about. Unfortunately, he rather has me over a barrel. His father owns the largest television network in California and it would be an unbelievably bad move on my part not to include him. I hope you are okay with that, Max.

"I'm not sure he would try too hard. He won't have much incentive, if Daddy is so rich. But at the end of the day, you are the one who is making this happen. I'm not really going to oppose any of your decisions. Unless, of course, I am dead against them. Who knows, maybe some dreadful catastrophe will befall him."

"As long as we get him back to his father in one piece when the show is over… or my career could be over."

"Oh, I guess we could patch him up before we send him back!" Max giggled as he opened the next envelope. "Breena Mathis, wow, she's going to be a heartbreaker when she is older."

"She certainly is."

"Sounds like a ballsy little thing, too. I bet she is not scared of anything and could really kick butt if needed."

"I agree. I liked the ghost-hunter ambition part. I reckon she will play up to the cameras to make a good impression."

"Agreed, Muir. I like her, too. Right, two left – who have we got next? Zach Hamilton. That's a good strong name, if ever I heard one."

"Strong personality, going by his profile. Must have been tough growing up without a father. Sounds like he has turned out on the right side of the tracks, though. He is probably my favourite of the five. He needs to settle his demons and make his mother proud. A good American boy, and a local lad."

"He couldn't be more perfect. You have done a great job with these, Muir. Right, last one. Frankie Hatter. Another local by the looks of it. She's been inside the hall before – that could be useful."

"Yeah and she wants to settle some sort of family disagreement by proving the place is not haunted. We can have real fun making her believe otherwise."

"Sounds familiar," Max said.

"What does?"

"Oh, nothing. A friend of mine has some family disagreement going on, too – must be a lot of it about. Nothing for you to concern yourself with."

"Fine. So, what do you think? Do you want to see any of the other applications?"

"I don't think I need to, Muir. You and your assistant have done a magnificent job. I am happy with all five of your choices."

"Shall I have my assistant contact them and give them the good news, then?"

"I think so. All really good choices. I can't wait to meet them."

And somehow, Max meant it. Initially, he could not have given a damn who the five kids were, but now, having studied their letters and got to know them as real people, he could not have been happier. With the exception of one, they sounded like good kids, and Muir certainly knew his business. It bought everything home to Max that the programme was actually going to happen and he was a big step closer to his goal. Things could not have been better.

"How did everything go at the hall this afternoon?" Muir asked Gil at dinner that night.

"Great, I did a thorough recce of the two treatment rooms in the basement with the team, as they missed them yesterday. We had a good delve into everything down there. Most of the stuff was unimaginably horrific. The treatments must have been totally inhumane."

"And how did the planning go?" Muir asked.

"Very well. We managed to work out the basement and the ground floor. We will head back tomorrow and hopefully get the first floor and attic sorted. When we get back to New York, we will computerise as much as we can in advance of the show and edit what we already have."

"Do you have everything you need?"

"Not quite. I called the studio earlier; we are having some furniture, some more lighting and a couple more generators sent down, plus all the electronics and wiring for the control room."

"Good, that's Max's department. On the night of the show, Max, we are planning a control room somewhere in the hall that only you will have access to. From there, you will have control of the cameras and microphones in each of the rooms. The live feed to all the rooms will be from there, too. So, the audience will see what you see."

"All sounds a little technical for me, I'm afraid."

"Don't worry, Max, I will talk you through how everything works in a technical run-through the day we air," Gil explained. "What about Imogen? Will she play any part on the day?"

"I don't think that will be necessary. Imogen has played her part by introducing us all to the hall," Max cut in, before Imogen had a chance.

"Yes, Max is right. You chaps won't need me hanging around, getting under your feet." Imogen understood Max would not want her in the hall on the night of the show.

"Well, Imogen, the day before we air, the crew will drive down in the network bus. It will contain all the added extras required for the show. It is a mobile studio, if you like, for hair, make-up – that sort of thing. The crew can also sleep in it, if necessary. You are welcome to camp out there with me or wait in the production trailer with Gil while the show goes ahead, if you wish," Muir offered.

"Yes, thank you. I would be happy with either. Now, if you will excuse me, gentlemen, I would like an early night. If you need me at the hall tomorrow, perhaps you will let me know in the morning."

That night, a violent storm erupted high above the guesthouse. The following morning, after a turbulent night's sleep, all of the guests were tired.

"It's still pouring out there. Should we wait until it eases off before we head out to the hall, Boss?" Gil asked, when he found Muir in the lounge, having missed breakfast.

"I've just had a call from New York and I have to get back there tomorrow to sort a scheduling problem. If you do a full day at the house today, do you think you can get everything finished by tonight?"

"Yes, I think so, if we knuckle down."

"Good. We can head back to New York first thing in the morning then. You get the crew out to the hall as soon as you can and get a head start. I will follow on shortly. I have to call Carol before I leave. I can bring Imogen and Max, too. See you shortly."

Gil bumped into Imogen in the reception area and explained they would be heading back to New York the next day. She felt a wave of disappointment to hear they were leaving so soon. The circumstances that had brought them together were far from ideal, but she liked Gil. She had only just met him and knew nothing of his personal life, but knew she would miss seeing him every day.

"It's a shame we have to head back earlier than planned," Gil said, as though he had read her mind. "Muir needs to go back and we are almost done here for the time being. At least we have the show to come back for, though. I wonder, if we have time between filming, could we grab a drink together?"

"Yes, Gil, I would like that. Thank you."

As he splashed his way to the car, Imogen watched him and suddenly remembered the last time she had let a man buy her a drink. Somehow, she did not believe that doing so with Gil would have the same outcome as it had with Max, and she looked forward to the prospect of it immensely.

"Yes, that's right, call Bracken and tell him I will be back in New York tomorrow afternoon and the scheduling will be sorted by the following lunchtime." Imogen heard Muir on the telephone as she entered the guesthouse lounge. "Then, please call the five final contestants that we have chosen for the Hacker Hall show. I have sent you an email with their contact details, but I want a personal touch. Please mention we would like them in New York for a screen test on 28th and 29th of this month, and they need to be available to travel to Pennsylvania on 13th of next month for the live show. Explain that all expenses, accommodation and flights will be taken care of – and then get on and book their hotels and tickets. If any of them have any problems with the dates, please let me know, but hopefully they should all be available or they wouldn't have applied, and I will see you tomorrow afternoon."

"I just saw Gil heading off to the hall. I gather you will be finished here tonight," Imogen said, when Muir finished his call.

"Yes, I have an issue in New York so I need to get back, and Gil is pretty sure he will wrap everything up today, too."

"Sounds like everything is coming together nicely."

"It certainly is. I was just speaking to my assistant. She will be calling the five chosen applicants today and arranging for them to come to New York. I really am excited to meet them all. It will be a big step forward."

"I will look forward to meeting them, too. I guess that will be on the night of the show."

"You are very welcome to join Max in New York when we bring them over for the screen tests."

"Thank you, Muir, but I think I had better pass. Daddy's campaign is hotting up, so I will probably be needed here, if that's okay?" Imogen did not relish another trip to New York, or anywhere, with Max, although she could not tell that to Muir.

"Of course it is, Imogen. Your father sounds like a wonderful man. When we are here for the show, it would be a pleasure if you had the time to introduce us. I would very much like to meet him."

"Sure. If we have the time, I can't see it would be a problem."

"Super. Also, Imogen, while I have you here, I would like to say thank you for your input and help with this project. This is something completely new for our network and we are all extremely excited about it. Max, too, of course. It will bring a lot of publicity and kudos our way, putting us in competition with some of the larger New York networks if we pull this off – which, of course, we will. And we have you to thank for that. If you had not told Max about the hall and given him all the information about it, the show would never have got off the ground. So, thank you. Thank you very much."

"You are welcome, Muir. I really hope the show brings you all the success you expect from it." And Imogen meant it, knowing that with Max on board, anything could happen. She only hoped that his warped, twisted plan did not jeopardise things for Muir. He was a nice man and did not deserve Max's treachery.

"Right, I'm heading out to the hall, now I've finished my calls. Would you like to come, too, as it's our last day here for a while?"

"Yes, thanks. It's not where I would normally choose to spend my days, you understand, but I would like to come." Even being in the house of horrors was bearable, if it meant she could spend a fraction more time with Gil before he left.

"Morning, you two. Would like to come where?" Max walked into the room with a steaming mug in his hand. "What a rotten night! That storm had me awake for hours. Had to run into the kitchen and grab a coffee to bring me round."

"Imogen and I are just about to head out to the hall. We are finishing up today and heading back to New York tomorrow. Do you want to join us?"

"I could do with catching up on some sleep, but yes, I wouldn't miss it for the world," Max said, placing his coffee mug on the table. "I will grab my jacket and meet you in the car."

Once at the hall, Imogen, Muir and Max found the crew in the attic. Gil decided to start at the top and work his way down. They had gone through all the storage compartments in the eaves and checked to see if they could use any of the old furniture they found elsewhere in the house. From everything they had seen so far, considering the house had been locked up for one hundred years, most of the contents were in good condition. The design of the house and everything that had been left in place when the house closed would make the lives of the crew much easier. The production was quite a straightforward process once the special effects were added.

"Hello," Gil said with a smile as he saw Imogen, Muir and Max appear from the stairwell.

"Hello, Gil, we guessed you would be up here, after we wandered around the first floor briefly without finding you," Muir said.

"We are almost done up here. We were about to head back down."

"So, you are getting on nicely?"

"Yes, we can use some of the furniture from up here in some of the sparser rooms. Oh, and before I came up, I double-checked the floor plan against the actual rooms and I have found the perfect room for the control room."

"Excellent. Which one have you decided on?"

"I tried to find a room with as few doors as possible and somewhat out of the way, so it is less likely to be stumbled upon by the children. In the far-left corner of the ground floor is the old doctors' meeting room. It is large enough to take all the equipment and only has two doors. One internal into a bedroom and one leading outside, at the back of the house."

"Sounds perfect," Max said. "Only one door to keep locked on the inside, which is quite unusual in itself, and one so I can exit the house freely, without running the risk of bumping into anyone."

"Good work, Gil. Well done."

"No worries, Muir."

The group spent the next two hours fully exploring and examining the rooms of the first floor, once again working through lunchtime. The time passed quickly with the team feeling the excitement mounting, the more plans they made. All except Imogen; she found the whole thing rather boring as she followed the men around, unable to contribute as she knew nothing of the effects and trickery they discussed.

Max could see from her face that she had seen enough of the house and would have been happy to make her exit.

"Boys, if you don't mind, before we finish up today, I would like to spend some more time down in the basement," Max asked purposely to annoy Imogen, as he knew how much she hated it down there.

"Sure. Anything of particular interest down there?"

"No, not really. I feel that with it being the most gruesome part of the house, the children may be extra fascinated by it. They may be inclined to spend a lot of time down there. So, I want to have a thorough picture of it in my head, however disturbing."

"You are probably right, Max. Good thinking. We will head down when we have finished here and then we should have everything we need," Gil acknowledged.

Within half an hour, the group made their way down the two flights of stairs and into the basement. They followed Max as he boldly made his way into the nearest treatment room. Some of the crew dispersed into the second treatment room and a couple into the morgue. Imogen walked, as if drawn, towards the copper bath in the centre of the room.

"Did you move anything when you were in here yesterday, Max?" Imogen seemed a little distressed.

"No. Why? What's the matter?"

"Look, the bath… The dipper hoist has moved from the last time we were here. The chair has been lowered into the bath."

"It could easily have been moved by someone else visiting since then. It could even have been from a draft in this rickety old place."

"No! You are wrong. Look, there too… that trolley should not be there. And those tong things – everything looks different. I'm getting a bad feeling in the pit of my stomach. Gil, can we please leave—"

The next thing Imogen saw was a dazzling white light, which blinded her vision for a second or two. As the radiant mist cleared, Imogen stood, transfixed, looking at a woman wearing a hospital gown, her hands behind her back. The room was fresh and bright, and a spotlight shone, illuminating everything around her. A small, suited man busily shuffled objects around before he moved towards the woman. She seemed to be in a deep trance as he escorted her towards the chair attached to the dipper hoist. Oblivious to Imogen's presence, he turned the dazed woman around to face him, in order to lower her carefully onto the chair. The woman, it seemed, had other ideas. Swiftly, from behind her back, her arm swung around and the hammer she held met violently with the side of the man's head. With some difficulty, she lifted his lifeless frame from the floor and strapped it to the chair that had been prepared for her. Knowing exactly what to do, as if she had seen the procedure a thousand times before, the woman manoeuvred the hoist, shifted the chair over the copper tub and slowly lowered it – and its inhabitant – into the water.

Thankfully, still unconscious, the man in the water had no idea of what was about to happen. The woman picked up a pair of tong-like paddles from the nearby trolley. Carefully and precisely, she dropped them into the water. Next, she slowly moved behind the bath, bent down and pulled a small lever.

Instantly, the room flared into a blaze of sparks, emanating from the water. The body in the chair began to writhe and shudder violently, whilst the man's skin sizzled and burnt before Imogen's eyes. The woman, aloof and detached, watched, unaffected, as the man's skin quickly scorched all over. Finally, with a satisfied grin, she turned and left the room.

"Oh my God… how horrible…" Imogen put her hands to her nose, as if she could smell the burning flesh. "Please, come on, we must leave."

"Imogen, are you okay? You look like you've seen a ghost. What on earth just happened?" Gil asked, rather concerned.

"Did any of you see that? Please tell me you saw it. It was horrible. Please, I have to get out of here now," Imogen said, as she headed straight for the door and then the stairs.

Outside, when they were all finally free of the house, Gil, Muir and Max tried to ascertain what had happened in the basement.

"Really, did none of you see the woman and the man? She lowered him into the tub and threw in… God, it was awful. His body just fried to ashes. Please. One of you must have seen it?" Imogen almost pleaded.

"Oh, you poor thing. It sounds terrible," Gil said, gently putting his arm around her shoulders.

"Honestly, Imogen, I don't believe any of us saw anything. Surely, with everything we have seen, your imagination played a trick on you," Muir concluded.

"No, I didn't see it either, but I reckon it was old Hacker himself, when he met his doom at the hands of Elizabeth Brute. Sounds exactly how the stories tell it," Max told them.

"Good God, Max. Do you really think so?" Muir was shocked, but not convinced.

"It certainly sounds like it. Maybe the house is haunted, after all."

"Enough of the haunted nonsense, Max. The poor girl is shaken enough. Let it drop now," Gil said, sternly. "I think I should take Imogen back to the guesthouse. She has had enough for one day. Max, would you be kind enough to tell the boys we have left and come back with them when they are done here?" He wanted to get Imogen away from Max and not give him the chance to argue. "Muir, you had better come with us, as the other two cars will be full. Make sure you lock up securely. We will see you back at the guesthouse, Max."

"Thank you for bringing me back," Imogen said, once they had arrived at the guesthouse.

"Would you like a drink or something to eat?" Muir asked.

"No, thanks. If you don't mind, I'm a bit out of sorts. I think I will head to my room, have a hot bath and get an early night."

When Max and the others arrived, they all met for an early dinner and chatted about everything they had achieved over the previous few days. Muir was pleased with the quick progress that had been made. Max was pleased his plan was coming together so easily. Imogen had played her part and not let anything slip, even if she'd had a slight wobble that afternoon. None of them had any idea what had made her react so oddly. However, the one thing Max was certain of was that the hall was not haunted. He and the team had spent a great deal of time there over the last few days with, as far as he was concerned, no evidence of ghostly behaviour.

The crew were now done with all the preparations for the show. The next morning Muir and his team would be heading back to New York to put their findings and plans together, and in four weeks' time, Max's show would take to the airwaves, making him a very rich man.

On the final morning of the stay at the guesthouse in Hackers Hollow, everyone was in a much better frame of mind after a calmer night's sleep. Imogen's episode of the previous afternoon was not mentioned and talk was mostly concerned with the next four weeks leading up to the live show.

"Will you need me for anything else before the show, Muir?"

"Yes, Max. I would like you to meet the children before the day of the show. When we have final confirmation that all five are on board, I will bring them to New York to get them in front of the camera and fill them in on the details of the programme. I think it would be a good idea to have you there, if you have the time."

"Time, I have plenty of. It's money that is in short supply."

"Do not worry, Max. All expenses are on the network. And you will have your fee on the day of the show. Also, if we have a hit on our hands, your face will be in great demand in the future. I have a feeling you won't have to worry about a lack of money after the show airs."

"Funny, I have the same feeling. I think you may be right." When the show was over, he would not need his face to be in great demand. Max would be a rich man, regardless. "Let me know when you want me and I will be there."

"Would you mind if I pass on that trip, Muir? I would like to stay close to home in case I am needed here," Imogen asked.

"Of course, I think we can manage without you. I will look forward to seeing you when we return. We will be back in Pennsylvania the day before the show and I will have my assistant book the guesthouse for all of us again, including the children. Obviously the two local kids can travel home if they wish, but the others will have to stay."

"Will you need us to help with anything when you return?"

"No thanks, Imogen. I doubt it. When the whole crew are here – sound, production, photography, make-up, costume, showrunners, editors, mixers and all – you will be able to sit back and enjoy watching our TV show come to life. I think you will be surprised at how thrilling it can be, especially a live show."

"I can't wait. It all sounds incredibly exciting."

"Right then. The cars are packed and we are ready to roll. Max, Imogen, thanks for all your help over the last few days. Imogen, we will see you in four weeks. Max, the children are expected in New York at the end of the month. I will call you with the arrangements."

Max and Imogen followed Muir, Gil and the rest of the team to the front door and watched as they climbed into their vehicles. Gil had not had time to speak privately with Imogen, but had secretly squeezed her hand as he left the building and gave her an affectionate smile that said he looked forward to seeing her soon. Max just smiled. Everything was working out exactly as planned.

"Things are looking up, Imogen, my dear. Just a few more weeks and we will have our reward."

"You will, you mean. I've told you before I don't want anything to do with your sordid plan or the money. I think it is so wrong, the way you are manipulating all those people, especially the children."

"Look. Why do you think the children are doing it, and why did the network take on the show in the first place? They are all in it for the money. What I am doing and what they are doing, is not so different. If you had ever wanted for anything in your spoilt little life, Imogen, you would understand."

"I do understand. I understand that you are deceiving a lot of good people and I will never agree with you about that."

"God, Imogen, don't you ever get tired of being so perfect?"

"Oh, go to hell, Max."

"I will, Imogen, when I am extraordinarily rich. Now, collect your bags and I will return you to the comfort of home, where Mumsy and Dadda await."

FIVE

THE FINAL FIVE

"Zach, a woman telephoned for you today, from New York. She didn't leave a message. I told her you would be home around now, so she said she would call again," Mrs Hamilton told her son when he arrived home from his training session.

"Thanks. I'm not expecting anyone. I wonder who she is," Zach replied.

"You'll find out when she calls. How was training, by the way?"

"Great. My serve was really firing today," Zach told his mum as they walked to the kitchen and he removed his tennis shoes. "I'm just going to grab a quick shower. If the woman phones again, please ask her to hold on and call me."

"Sure, but don't be long, dinner is almost ready."

Zach wondered who it was that had called. He had no dealings with anyone in New York. He had only been there once when he was ten – a birthday surprise from his mum. Then, as he stepped into the shower, he remembered the advert he had replied to in *USA Today* a few weeks before. Suddenly, a moment of excitement engulfed him. Could his application have been successful? Surely they didn't call everyone, so it had to be good news in some way.

Not allowing himself to get carried away, Zach had the briefest shower in history. He had missed the call once and could not afford to risk missing the second. What if she could not get hold of him and the opportunity went to someone else? Zach was not prepared to let that happen.

The moment he had dried and wrapped himself in his bathrobe, he heard the telephone ring.

"It's okay, Mum, I will grab it up here," Zach said as he ran into his mother's room and launched himself across her bed to lift the receiver. "Hello."

"May I speak to Zach Hamilton, please?" the woman on the other end of the line asked.

"Yes, I'm Zach."

"Hello, Zach, I'm calling from MMNYTV in New York. You recently replied to an advert the network placed, to take part in a one-off TV show."

"That's right."

"Well, I have been asked to call you personally by the network owner, Mr Muir Mason, to advise you that he loved your application and you have been chosen as one of the five finalists."

"Wow! That's incredible, thanks." Zach tried to contain his excitement and sound cool. "So, what happens next?"

"Mr Mason will write to you with all the details, but I have been asked to inform you that you will be required to attend a screen test and briefing in New York on 28th and 29th of this month. Then the show will be on the 13th of next month in Pennsylvania."

"I think I know where the show will be held, as I wrote in my letter. Can you confirm that it will be at Hacker Hall? Be great, if it is. It is very local to me here."

"I shouldn't really divulge any of the details. Mr Mason will do that when you come for the briefing, so don't let on you heard it from me. Yes, it is Hacker Hall. Now, can you make the dates for New York, and will you need to be accompanied?"

"You bet. I will be there. I have a long-standing score to settle. Bring it on. Oh, and no thanks to accompaniment, Mum will be happy for me to make the trip alone."

"Super, Zach. Mr Mason will send the trip details and tickets through in the next few days. I look forward to meeting you when you get to New York."

"Yeah, me too. And thanks very much," Zach said, as he replaced the phone. He took a second to compose himself. His chance had finally come to get inside the house that had plagued his conscience for so long. And if he won the money, that would be an extra bonus.

"Mum! Mum! I'm in! The show at Hacker Hall. I've been picked for the show and I'm off to New York!" he screamed as he charged down the stairs.

"Yes, hello," Breena's grandmother said, when her telephone rang.

"May I speak to Breena Mathis, please?" the woman on the line asked.

"She is doing her homework. This is her grandmother, Mrs Carney, speaking. Can I help you?"

"I'm calling from MMNYTV in New York. She recently answered an advert the network placed, to take part in a one-off television show. Do you know about that?"

"Yes, of course. Breena is a good girl. She tells her old gran everything."

"Well, Mrs Carney, I would really like to speak to her about it, if I can, please."

"Breena is a minor, you know, so if you don't mind you had better give me the information." Muir's assistant quickly realised there was no way that this strict-sounding woman was going to bring Breena to the phone.

"That's not a problem. I have been asked to call her personally by the network owner, Mr Muir Mason, to advise that her application was successful and she has been chosen as one of the five finalists."

"That is exciting. I know she will be delighted. She has talked about nothing else since she sent the letter."

"Mr Mason will write to her with all the details, but I have been asked to inform you that she will be required to attend a screen test and briefing in New York on 28th and 29th of this month. Then the show will be on the 13th of next month in Pennsylvania."

"That shouldn't be a problem. We have little in the diary these days."

"And as Breena is only thirteen, she needs to be accompanied. Will you be coming with her, Mrs Carney?"

"Yes, most assuredly. She cannot make a trip like that on her own."

"I wonder if perhaps another family member may be better suited to the task?"

"I don't understand why. We do everything together."

"I can't say too much, but the show is based in an old house that some say is haunted. The children will be put in some quite frightening situations. It will not be viewing for the fainthearted." Muir's assistant, Carol, tried to be as diplomatic as possible.

"I see what you are getting at. Poor old lady; can't handle the situation. Just you listen to me. People of my generation are made of sterner stuff than the youth of today. There is nothing I have not seen in my long life."

"Very well, if you are certain. I will ensure you have a front row seat in the live audience. Mr Mason will send the trip details and tickets through in the next few days. There will also be a consent form that needs to be completed and brought with you. Thank you, Mrs Carney, and please tell Breena I look forward to meeting her when you get to New York."

"Thank you; we will see you on 28th," Mrs Carney said, as she put down the receiver. "Breena, dear, come down a moment will you. I have great news. You will not believe who just called."

"You have reached the Fortune residence. Neither Johnson, Madeline nor Henry are available to take your call at present. Please be kind enough to leave your telephone number and a brief message after the tone, and one of us will get back in contact at our earliest convenience."

Typical, thought Carol, as she put the phone down, without leaving a message. The sort of people that are just too busy to answer. Someone ought to be home. It was approaching dinnertime in LA, but one never quite knew what the extraordinarily rich got up to. Probably eating out every night. *One last attempt*, she told herself; *then it would have to wait until the next morning*. She had stayed at the office until nine o'clock to make the call as late as possible. Now she wanted her dinner and her bed.

"Hola! Fortuna residence," came a voice with a strong Mexican accent.

"Hello. Can I please speak with Henry Fortune?"

"Si senora. I get for you. Please wait."

As Carol waited on the line, she heard a youthful voice shouting. He seemed most perturbed that Margarita, who she assumed was a maid, had not asked who was calling.

"Yes, who is this?" came the angry young man's voice eventually.

"Hello. I'm calling from MMNYTV in New York. I have been asked to call you by Mr Muir Mason, the network owner, regarding your application to take part in a one-off TV show."

"Couldn't he have called me himself, rather than getting one of his minions to do it?"

Carol had been warned about this applicant, and she could already tell from the first few seconds of their conversation that she did not like this boy.

"He is out of New York, working on the show, although that is not your concern. He has asked me to let you know that you have been successfully chosen, with four others, to appear on the show."

"Of course I have. It was never in doubt. Father would have had a lot to say about it if I had not been chosen. So, when do you want me? I can fly in on father's private jet."

"I'm sure you can," she answered, sarcastically. "Mr Mason needs you in New York on 28th and 29th of this month and then in Pennsylvania for the show, two weeks later, on the 13th. Is that suitable?"

"Yeah, yeah. No problem. And before you ask, I will be fine to travel alone. I have been on the jet on my own many times in the past. Also, the hotel had better be a good one. I am not sharing with the other contestants. I want my own room."

"Anything you say, Master Fortune." She made a point of using the title master as she felt sure it would aggravate him. There was also a lot more she wanted to say but knew it was not worth it. It would be wasted on a child such as Henry Fortune. "Mr Mason will send the trip details through in the next few days. There will also be a consent form that needs to be completed and brought with you."

"I shouldn't worry about unnecessary things like that. Father will telephone Mr Mason and tell him everything is okay. Now, if there is nothing else, I'm terribly busy here."

"No, nothing else. We will see you in New York on the 28th then. Goodbye," Carol said, happy to put down the telephone.

As she closed up the office and made her way home, her only thought was that she hoped, above all else, that Henry Fortune did not win the money.

The following morning, Carol arrived early at the network. Muir was due back at some stage during the afternoon, so she had plenty of work to catch up on before his return. She also wanted to contact the last two finalists before they headed out for the day.

"Good morning, please may I speak to Cait Luu?" she said, after dialling the fourth number.

"Yes, Cait speaking."

"Hello Cait. I'm calling from the office of Mr Muir Mason, owner of MMNYTV here in New York. He has asked me to call you regarding your reply to an advert the network placed, to take part in a one-off TV show."

"My goodness. Is something wrong?"

"Oh no. On the contrary, Miss Luu, I am pleased to be able to tell you that you have been chosen as one of the five finalists."

"Really? Are you sure?" Cait struggled to believe what she was hearing.

"I certainly am. Mr Mason will write to you with all the details, but I have been asked to advise you that you will be required to attend a screen test and briefing here at the network on 28th and 29th of this month. Then the show will be on the 13th of next month in Pennsylvania."

"I am ever so sorry, but I never expected to be chosen. I'm not sure that I will be able to commit to the time off. The academy is incredibly strict. Would you mind holding for a minute while I tell my mum what you have said?"

"Yes, of course. But before you do, I would like to add that Mr Mason was most impressed with your letter. Off the record, he told me that yours was his favourite of all the applications and I know, for a fact, that he would be extremely disappointed if you were unable to make it."

"Thank you, that's kind. I won't keep you a moment."

The wait was silent as Muir's assistant hung on the line. She had expected to be able to hear the voices discussing the situation, but Cait must have left the room to speak to her mother. While she waited, her main worry was that this polite young lady was so lacking in confidence she would back out from fear.

"Hello. Sorry to keep you waiting."

"Not a problem, Cait. Is everything agreed with your mother?"

"Yes. I told her what you said and she thinks it will be a wonderful opportunity for me. She is going to speak to my madame and request the time off for Pennsylvania, and if I could come by and do the screen test after school, that would be amazing. And could my mum please come to Pennsylvania with me?"

"Oh yes, Cait. I don't see any problem with you coming by after school. It's lucky you are in New York. And yes, your mum is very welcome. Mr Mason will be pleased. He is very much looking forward to meeting you. He will send through everything you need to know in the next few days. There will also be a consent form for your mother to sign. Please bring that when you come for the screen test."

"I will – and thank you. I look forward to meeting you."

"And you, Cait, and you."

How could two children be so different? Carol wondered, after she replaced the phone. A young boy who had everything materialistically, but lacked decorum, graciousness and manners; and a young girl, who had to work hard for all she had, yet was brimming with all three attributes and probably many more.

Still smiling to herself after the conversation with Cait, Carol picked up the phone again. One last call to make and then she could get on with her work.

"Good morning. Could I please speak to Frankie Hatter?" Muir's assistant asked as she poured herself a cup of coffee, from the pot next to her desk.

"Yes, I'm Frankie. Who is this? It's okay, Mum, it's for me," she screamed down the phone. "Sorry about that. It's a bit mad here in the mornings, trying to get out to school and stuff."

"Yes, of course. I will try to be quick. I'm calling from MMNYTV in New York. You recently applied to the network to take part in a one-off TV show, and I'm happy to tell you that you have been chosen as one of the final five contestants."

"Oh my God! That's fantastic." Frankie then suddenly started to whisper. "I don't have much time. Can you briefly tell me what I need to do now?"

"Mr Mason will write to you with all the details. He asked that I inform you that you will be required to attend a screen test and briefing here at the network on 28th and 29th of this month. Then the show will be on the 13th of next month in Pennsylvania."

"Great, thanks. That is all I need for now. I'm sorry I really have to go," she said, still speaking incredibly quietly. "Could you please send me everything I need to know by letter? Oh, and please mark it private. Sorry, my mum is coming. I have to run. Thank you."

"Who was that on the phone so early, Frances?" Frankie's mum asked as she entered the hall.

"Oh, nothing. It was Tilly ringing to remind me to speak to you about a school trip to New York on the 28th and 29th."

"It's the first I've heard of it."

"I know. We haven't had the letter yet. We only just talked about it in class. I will know more when I get the letter from my teacher."

"Good, we'll talk about it then. Now, come on, we must be going or you will be late."

Muir arrived back in New York at four in the afternoon. He took a taxi straight to the studio. He entered his office, closed the door behind him and stared out of the window. The view was a peaceful one, high above the crowds and busy streets below. As he watched the trees that surrounded the Jacqueline Kennedy-

Onassis Reservoir in Central Park blow in the wind, his thoughts were interrupted by a soft knock on the office door.

"Welcome back, Mr Mason. Can I get you a cup of coffee?" Carol stuck her head around the door. "Oh, sorry. I didn't mean to disturb you."

"Not a problem, Carol. I was just thinking about Pennsylvania. God, what a weird experience. Of all my years in the television industry, I have never seen anything quite like that house in Hackers Hallow. The smell. The atmosphere. Everything about it. Walking around and seeing all the furniture and equipment still in place, brought the place to life. You can only imagine what kind of torment and persecution went on there."

"Sounds charming," Carol said, with a sarcastic tone.

"Not a word I would use. You have to see it to believe it. You know I don't believe in anything paranormal, but I have to admit, there were a couple of things that freaked me out. It certainly made me wonder."

"I'm sure it was nothing really. These things can usually be explained with science. And, surely, if it made you feel that way, that can only be good for the show. It will get the audience and the contestants asking questions and maybe scare the pants off them."

"You are right about that. I can honestly say, though, I'm glad Max will be the one in the hall on the night. I would be quite happy to never set foot in there again. Now, would you be kind enough to grab me that coffee, please? Then you can fill me in on what's been happening here."

The telephone rang as Carol left the room to fetch the coffee, and when she returned, Muir was deep in conversation. She placed his coffee down and left the room until he had finished.

"Safe to come in?" Carol asked, when she saw – through the glass divide – that he had replaced the receiver.

"Yes, of course. Thanks for the coffee. Now, what news of our fabulous five?"

"All spoken to and I'm pleased to report they are all on

board. I didn't get to speak directly with Breena Mathis. Her grandmother was very much in charge. She assured me she would give Breena all the information, though. Zach Hamilton and Cait Luu seem like really good kids. I don't think they will cause you any problems. That Henry Fortune, however, is a totally different kettle of fish. A right piece of work, if you ask me. He will have to be watched carefully. Definite potential to upset the other children. And Frankie Hatter. I couldn't put my finger on it, but I had an odd feeling. Sweet enough; though I couldn't help thinking that something was not quite right when I spoke to her."

"Hey, everyone's different. It will be an advantage to have a variety of personalities. The audience will quickly make up their minds as to which ones they like and dislike. But you're right, from what I know of him, I don't think the Fortune boy will be too popular. The only thing we can hope is that if he wins the money, he will give it to charity. It's not like he needs it."

"I can't see that happening somehow. Rich people love money," Carol stated.

"Never a truer word spoken. Now, what else?" Muir asked.

"I spoke to Mr Bracken and he is expecting to see you in his office for an early lunch meeting tomorrow at twelve. And a new tender came in. A Boston-based production company is looking for a network to pilot a potential new medical drama. I have the details for you to call them back."

"Thanks, Carol. All sounds fine. Please call Bracken to confirm the meeting tomorrow and email me the info on the medical drama. I will look over it at home tonight. It's been a long day with the journey back from Pennsylvania, so I will head home shortly."

"Sure, no problem."

"And – jobs for tomorrow. Time is ticking on, so I want you to concentrate on everything for the House of a Hundred Doors project. Book the Courtyard Marriott for the children and their guardians, if they are bringing any, for an overnight stay on 28th."

"Oh, that reminds me. Cait Luu is worried about taking time out of the academy, so she would like her screen test after school. And obviously she doesn't require a hotel."

"Yes, I don't see any problems there. So, book for everyone else. Book their flights and prepare a confirmation letter with itinerary for each, including the consent forms. I will check them before we send them out. And lastly, book the Hackers Hollow Guesthouse for the night of the 13th, after the show. As well as the children, please book a room for me, Max and Imogen Hackerton, and then all the flights to Pennsylvania. That should keep you busy for most of the day. I will see you briefly in the morning before I head to Bracken's office. Thanks, Carol, have a good evening."

"You, too, Mr Mason. See you tomorrow."

As Muir took the short walk back to his apartment, he could not remove the thoughts of Hacker Hall from his mind. This show, if as successful as everyone expected, would make a small fortune for his network and bring in new clients from all angles. However, success usually came at a price. And now, having been to Hacker Hall, the price was making a TV show in such a degraded and monstrous place. The few short days he and his crew had spent there had already taken a toll on his mind.

As he turned the key to enter his penthouse, with an even more spectacular view of Central Park than his office, he convinced himself that Carol was right. Most things could be explained with science and the odd things that happened were probably nothing.

Six

SCREEN TESTS

The next two weeks passed quickly for Imogen, without a word from Max. She knew the time for him to visit New York to meet the five children for the show was approaching and she expected that she would hear from him before too long.

She had been working at her father's campaign office. Early indications were that he had a strong lead in the polls and was in line to become the next Senator of Pennsylvania. For her father and her whole family, it had been a lifelong ambition and now, thanks to a lot of hard work, it looked as though it was actually going to happen.

Looking around the office, admiring the posters that hung on the walls, she saw her father's face smiling broadly back at her. Max entered her head once again. She knew what he was doing was wrong. He was a despicable man, whom she wished she had never met. Even so, she was stuck in a situation and had to carry it through. For her sake, her father's sake and for the Hackerton family name.

She loved her parents dearly, having been given a wonderful childhood – wanting for nothing. She remembered family holidays in Europe and Hawaii, and the time they bought ponies for her tenth and Astrid's eighth birthdays. They had always been an incredibly close and loving family until the day, at seventeen, Astrid had informed her parents she was pregnant. David Hackerton was well underway with his political career by then and the news had rocked the family's foundation.

The boy concerned offered no assistance in the matter and Imogen's parents tried, in vain, to talk Astrid into having a termination. They believed that an unmarried daughter with a baby would harm any chance of a successful political career for her father. Astrid had other ideas. She wanted her baby and nothing they did nor said would make her change her mind.

Since then, twelve years had passed and the relationship between Astrid and her parents was still strained. Astrid had never fully forgiven them for not supporting her and whenever they came into contact, they argued, leaving Imogen caught in the middle between the parents she adored and the sister she missed.

Pondering about Astrid, and how she believed her parents should look for the money and own up to their ancestry, Imogen's mind returned to Max. She wondered how, after the show, the whole sorry mess was going to end.

"Imogen, telephone," one of the campaign officers cut into her thoughts.

"Thanks. Any idea who it is?"

"No, sorry. He just said he was calling from New York."

That gave Imogen three options: Gil, Muir or Max. Gil? It certainly would not be him, although she wished it were. He did not have her number. Muir? He had no reason to be calling her. All the dealings for the show were sorted directly with Max. And thirdly, Max himself. It had to be him. Unfortunately.

"Hello! Imogen Hackerton speaking."

"Imogen, hi. Maxi baby here. How you doing?"

"I was having a perfect day until the phone rang," she replied. It was as if he had sensed he was on her mind.

"Ha ha, very funny. Hey, listen, I've just arrived in New York and wanted to keep you abreast of everything. I would hate you to think I had forgotten about you or that you were missing out on anything."

"Perhaps I was hoping you had forgotten all about me."

"No chance of that, I'm afraid. You know how important you are to me, Imogen. Well, anyway, I'm here and due to meet the contestants tomorrow. We are going to run them through a try-out behind the camera and fill them in on what they can expect once they get to Hacker Hall. Imogen, we are nearly there. Just two weeks from now, we will all be together again in Pennsylvania. I will have my money and you will have your life back. Isn't it exciting?"

"Yes, Max, I'm ecstatic," she said, yawning. "Just call me when you have the final details of the show and I will play my part."

"You betcha. Looking forward to it. Two weeks and counting. Call you soon."

On 28th April, Muir arrived at the network while the early morning spring dew still rested on the grass in Central Park. Carol had arranged for a buffet lunch to be brought in and had tidied the office, almost beyond Muir's recognition.

The children who were travelling from out of state were expected around lunchtime, with Cait following on about three o'clock in the afternoon. The time of Henry's arrival was anyone's guess. He was due to be picked up by limousine when his father's private jet landed, and Muir guessed he would be a law unto himself. Johnson Fortune had called the week before and assured Muir of his cooperation, requesting that he was to provide Henry with anything he desired while he was in New York. Muir understood that he had to play into Henry's hands, but he was certainly not going to let a spoilt fourteen-year-old boy run rings around him. He had a show to make and Muir was not going to let anyone or anything distract him.

Max arrived from his hotel shortly after eleven and Carol showed him into Muir's office. Gil was already there going over the last few special effects that had been added to some of the rooms. The three men greeted each other and shook hands, and Carol disappeared to make fresh coffee.

"Good to see you, Max. Welcome back to New York. I hope the hotel is comfortable?" Muir asked.

"Sure is. Much nicer than where Imogen and I stayed on our last visit. Great breakfast, too. Good to see you, Gil. Everything ready for our show?"

"Almost. I was just showing Muir the final additions we have made to some of the rooms before the children arrive."

"Yes, Max, take a look at these." Muir turned Gil's laptop towards Max as he took a seat, while Carol re-entered with the coffee. "Thank you, Carol. That will be all for now. Would you please let us know when the contestants begin to arrive?"

"Yes, of course, Mr Mason," Carol said and closed the door on her way out.

"So, what do you think?" Muir asked, as Max watched the slideshow of the different rooms and their individual effects.

"Fantastic. The ideas are so varied. I have never seen anything like it. You and your team should be congratulated, Gil. If you can pull all this off at Hacker Hall, we will have a hit on our hands. The audience will love it. Well done."

"Thanks, Max. And have no doubts; we will pull it off. Now, if you will excuse me, I have work to do." Gil left Muir's office. He did not like Max and was happy to make his exit. There was something odd about him that Gil could not pinpoint. He only hoped that Muir was not getting himself into anything bad. He had seen the way Max had spoken to Imogen when they were in Pennsylvania and it had played on his mind. He hoped that once the show was over, Maximillion Crooked would vanish from their lives as swiftly as he had appeared.

"The images of the rooms look good, Muir. Can't wait to see the real thing on the night," Max said after Gil had left the room.

"They are good, aren't they? The boys have worked really hard on this, especially as it has been an unknown entity up to now. They have never had to put a show together outside the studio before. It is a first for all of us, Max, not just you."

"And you believe it will all come together on the day?"

"I have to believe it, Max. But if anyone can do it, Gil and his team can. They are the best special effects team on the East Coast."

"Well, when the show is a hit and the money rolls into the network, I reckon they will deserve a large bonus."

"I think you are right. Everyone's hard work will have to be acknowledged. Yes, come in, Carol," Muir said in response to a gentle tap on the door.

"Zach, Breena and Frankie have arrived. And I had a call from Johnson Fortune's secretary – Henry's plane has landed. He will be here in half an hour. Just one thing to note: Breena is with her grandmother, which we knew, but Frankie is on her own. Rather odd for a twelve-year-old, I thought. I had expected her mother to be with her."

"Thanks, Carol. We will be right out to meet them. Could you please call Gil and ask him to come up and give them a tour of the studio? Hopefully Henry will have arrived by then and we can get started."

"Right you are, Mr Mason," she said and left the room.

"Ready, Max? Let's meet the kids who are going to make our show a hit."

Max followed Muir from his office. They made their way to the small boardroom, where Carol had asked the children to wait.

At a quick glance, they were three normal-looking kids and Muir hoped he had made the right choices. He hoped they were up to the task.

"Good morning, everyone. I am Muir Mason and this is my associate, Maximillion Crooked. Thank you for coming and thank you very much for entering our competition. I would like to congratulate you on being successful; we very much look forward to working with you. Ah, Gil, good, you're here," Muir said, as Gil entered the room. "And this is Gil. He is head of our special effects team. We are still awaiting another contestant, so I thought Gil could give you a tour and show you what we do here. Then, when the young man arrives, we will have some lunch and get down to business."

The children and Breena's grandmother, Mrs Carney, nervously followed Gil around the network offices. They listened and watched attentively, without making any attempt to chat to one another. Gil suspected they were all rather scared and a little daunted at the situation, so he did his best to put them at ease. He showed them the sound and visual rooms. They met the camera crew and had a go at manoeuvring the cameras around, which was harder than it looked. They tried their hands at putting on some stage make-up and watched a comedy take as it was edited.

By the time the group arrived back at the boardroom, Muir's assistant had laid out the lunch and the children were all a lot more comfortable with their surroundings.

"Security have just called. Henry Fortune is on his way up," Carol whispered in Muir's ear, as a young, smartly dressed boy walked through the door.

"I hope you didn't wait for me; I ate on the jet," he shouted as he breezed confidently towards the group sitting in the boardroom. "Hello, everyone, I'm Henry Fortune. Just flew in from LA. Don't stand on ceremony. Do tuck in."

"Thank you for that," Muir spoke, sarcastically. "I'm Muir Mason. Welcome to my studio."

"Looks much smaller than Father's – but of course, it would. He does own the largest network in California." Everyone looked around the room, rather embarrassed by Henry's comment. He certainly was going to make an impression. "Can somebody get me a cup of coffee? I'm parched," he asked, rudely.

"There is a fresh pot next to my desk," Carol pointed, across from the boardroom. "Please help yourself." She was a very shrewd woman and had no intention of jumping to the demands of a spoilt teenage boy.

"Yes, grab yourself a coffee," Muir backed her up, "and then come and sit down. While we eat, we can all get to know each other a little better. This is Maximillion Crooked," Muir repeated his introduction for the sake of Henry. "He will be our presenter for the show and will be the only other person in the house other than the five of you. You will be meeting Cait, the fifth contestant, a little later, when she gets out of school. Now, I'm going to let Max tell you a little about the venue for the show."

"Hello again, it's a pleasure to have you all here," Max stepped forward. "You lucky five have been chosen from many thousands of applicants to play a daring and exciting game. The show will be revolutionary. A live show of this nature, in a venue such as this, has never been attempted before, so we are all entering a new and special world. The venue for the show will be a house called Hacker Hall in Pennsylvania." A murmur of voices broke out around the room, and Zach and Frankie nodded their heads, knowing they had been right in guessing the venue. "The house in question is a 19th-century lunatic asylum. I first learnt about the hall from a very dear friend of mine, whom you will all have the pleasure of meeting on the day of the show. She took me to visit the hall and I was struck immediately by two things. One, how awful it must have been to live in such a demonic institution. And two, how many doors the place had spread across all the rooms. This is why I nicknamed the place the 'House of a Hundred Doors.'"

"Are there a hundred doors?" Breena asked.

"Well, I did not get a chance to count, but it can't be far off. Anyway, walking around the house, I figured it would be the perfect venue for some sort of TV show, where contestants would step back to a more primitive time and search amongst the old furniture and pieces of gruesome equipment for something. Then, I thought, money. There had to be an incentive to make people want to take part and everyone loves the chance to win a prize – that is where the five of you come in. But don't underestimate that this building is pretty frightful in places. You will need a strong stomach. You will, of course, have the opportunity to decline going ahead, although we will need a firm answer from all of you before you leave New York tomorrow. Here are a few photos I have of the inside and outside of the house. Take a look and get a feel for the place. If you can't handle the pictures, you will never handle the real thing."

Max passed the photographs around the room and, again, a murmur of voices erupted. The children finally began to speak and interact with each other, while Mrs Carney shied away from the horrors she was being shown.

"Goodness gracious, Breena. These are awful. I'm not sure this is the sort of place you should be visiting."

"Nonsense, Gran. I can't wait to get in there. If I want to be a ghost-hunter, I had better get used to visiting places like this."

"Wow, you want to be a ghost-hunter. That is really cool," Zach said. "I have seen the hall from the outside. I used to walk past it to get to school."

"That makes you a local. I'm from Pennsylvania, too," Frankie entered the conversation. "And I have actually been in the house. These pictures are nothing. It's supposed to be haunted, you know."

"Haunted, rubbish. I don't think it will scare me. I think I will have something to eat, after all." Henry helped himself to a sandwich and finally took a seat.

"It's good to see you all starting to get to know each other," Muir told them. "Do any of you have any questions?"

"Will we be in teams?" Breena asked.

"I'm afraid not. Your competitive nature will be stronger if are working against each other."

"So, what happens if we meet each other by entering the same room?"

"If you meet another contestant, Zach, we hope you will just go about your search and move to another room."

"Where will we be looking?" Frankie asked this time.

"You are all free to move around the house, from room to room, looking in cupboards, furniture – anywhere you care to. Even under floorboards, if you wish."

"And the money, Muir, where will that be hidden?"

"It's Mr Mason to you, if you don't mind, Henry. If we tell you where the money is hidden, it wouldn't be much of a competition, would it? In fact, Max will be the only person who knows. Just before the show goes live, Max will enter the house and hide the bag with the cash, where he chooses. If none of the crew know, none of us can be accused of cheating or conspiring in favour of any of you."

"Very wise," Mrs Carney said, having sat quietly listening to all the questions until now. "What if any of the children get into difficulty of some kind?"

"Oh, Gran, don't be such a worrywart."

"No, no, Breena. It's a very valid question. We hope that will not happen, of course, Mrs Carney. Every room will have microphones and cameras, so the children will be seen and heard at all times. In the unlikely event of an emergency, the crew will only be a stone's throw away, outside the house. So, I would like you to be assured that we can reach the children within a few seconds." Muir wanted to reassure Breena's grandmother, knowing that if he had a child entering Hacker Hall, he would want to be confident of their safety, too. "Now, if you have all had enough to eat, shall we get ready to do a little filming?"

The group followed Muir and Max to the floor above, where they were met again by the camera crew they had seen before lunch. Muir told them they would take it in turns to speak into the camera, trying to be as natural as possible. Once in Hacker Hall, they would not be aware of the cameras and would go about their searching, oblivious to the fact they were being filmed. However, Muir wanted a shot of each of them for the advertisement to promote the programme, and to check they were relaxed and comfortable being filmed.

"I want to go first," Henry demanded. "I have been in front of the camera many times. I can show the others how it's done."

"How about we let the ladies go first? You will get your turn, Henry. Breena, would you like to go first? There is nothing to it, and with the career you seek, you will have to get used to being filmed. Just look into the camera and tell us your name, where you are from and a little about yourself," Muir told her.

"Sure, no problem."

And it wasn't. Breena was a natural. Her face lit up the second she began to speak. The whole room stood and watched with admiration, as she talked about how her love for horror movies had begun after she'd watched the 1976 version of *The Omen*, when she was just eight years old. She said her grandmother would have been furious if she had known, but she couldn't switch it off. She was hooked, and her love affair with the gory and the macabre had begun.

"Great job," Muir shouted, as she rejoined the group and everyone gave her a round of applause.

"Gosh, you made that look easy," Frankie told her.

"Nothing to it, really. Just be yourself and if you talk about something you love it will shine through."

"Wise words for one so young. Well done, that was excellent. Frankie, how about you next?" Muir asked.

"Sure, Mr Mason, but Breena will be a hard act to follow."

"You will be fine. There is nothing to worry about. Give it your best shot."

Frankie was a different personality from Breena and it was instantly clear. She did not seem quite as much at ease. She stared into the camera, transfixed – it was as though she thought that if she removed her eyes off the lens, the audience would not be able to see her.

"Frankie, try taking your eyes off the camera. Perhaps look around the room or at any of us. Try to forget the camera is there, in fact. That will make you feel more comfortable and will automatically put you at ease," Muir called across the room.

"Will do. Sorry."

"Nothing to be sorry for, just be yourself."

"I'm trying, but I don't know what to say."

"Look, Frankie, you are the only contestant who has been in the house, so that gives you an advantage in knowing your way around. How about telling us what you recall about it?" Muir said, encouragingly.

She began to walk around the room, rarely looking in the direction of the camera. Watching her, the small audience saw an instant change as she began to talk about Hacker Hall. She told of the day her mother had taken her there for a visit and the deep sadness and sense of misery she had felt moving around it, from room to room. She knew she was young; most people would have said she couldn't possibly understand what had gone on there. But Frankie was a bright, astute girl, and it would have been impossible not to be affected by the place, whatever the age.

Whilst there, her mother had taken some photos, which Frankie had taken into school for a show-and-tell lesson. Her classmates had been fascinated by what they saw. There was, of course, one reoccurring question. Was Hacker Hall haunted? And that was why Frankie had entered the competition. She was going to prove, once and for all, that Hacker Hall was not haunted.

"Well done," Muir said, as everyone clapped.

"Good job, Frankie. We knew you could do it," Zach told her, feeling a closeness to her as they came from the same town.

"Big deal. It's not like it's difficult or anything," Henry said, snidely.

"Thank you, Henry," Muir cut him off. "Just because you are fortunate to have been in this position before, please do not spoil it for those that haven't. And as you are so experienced, let's see what you're made of. You are up next."

"Cool, no problem," Henry said, confidently.

He moved in front of the camera and began to speak. He told the intimate audience that he lived in California with his shopaholic mother and his workaholic father, who owned the largest private television network in the west of the United States, which, of course, he had already told everyone in the room. He boasted about their beach house, his expensive private school and their army of servants that were put on earth to meet his every need – or so it seemed. Yes, Henry Fortune was confident in front of the camera. His audience considered it a cocky arrogance. He began telling the group why he was so sure he would beat the other contestants to take home the prize money, when Muir's assistant burst into the room and interrupted him in full flow.

"Mr Mason, Mr Crooked, Cait has arrived," Carol said, disturbing the group, which she would never have done if anyone other than Henry had been speaking. Closely behind, she was followed by a slim, elegant, oriental young woman.

"For goodness' sake. I was just getting to the interesting part." Henry was not pleased with the interruption.

"Thank you, Henry, you have said your piece." Muir shut him down. "Hello, Cait, please join us and meet the rest of the group. Allow me to introduce Maximillion Crooked, our show host.

And this is Frankie, Breena, Zach and that's Henry by the camera. Henry come over and join us. Take five, everyone," Muir called, before asking Carol to organise some afternoon tea.

Back in the boardroom, the children enjoyed hot chocolate, sodas and muffins. The five of them chatted amongst themselves and got to know each other. Muir looked on, noticing that Henry spoke the most and Cait spoke the least. He understood that Henry was proving to be an extrovert force and Cait had been introduced late to the group. He remembered, of course, from her application letter that she may have a confidence issue.

"Okay, guys, time is moving on. Shall we head back upstairs? Zach and Cait still have to perform for the cameras. Zach, perhaps you can go first, so Cait can see how it's done."

"Be happy to, Mr Mason. Come on, Cait, you and me together."

It had not escaped Zach's attention that Cait and he were a similar age, and that she was an extremely attractive young woman. Neither had it slipped him by that she seemed the least confident in the group. He wondered why such a quiet introvert would enter such a competition and throw herself into the limelight that was coming their way.

"If I'm honest, I'm a bit terrified of being filmed," Cait told Zach as they climbed back up the stairs, ahead of the rest of the group.

"You will be fine. I have never done it before either, but I can't imagine there is much to it. Mr Mason said you were late because you were coming along after school. I guess that means you live here in New York?"

"Yes, I'm on a ballet scholarship at The New York Performing Arts Academy."

"Wow, that's exciting. Surely that gives you experience in getting up in front of a crowd?" Zach asked.

"Well, yes, but I'm still not particularly good at it. My tutors are always on my back about building confidence. I thought, maybe, entering this competition would help."

"I'm sure everyone here will help you, too. They seem like a nice bunch. I'm sure even Henry must have some good attributes if we look hard enough." They both laughed as they entered the studio, already having Henry sussed. "I'm from Pennsylvania, so I know Hacker Hall. I used to walk past it on my way to school. I have always wanted to go inside, so this is an ideal opportunity for me."

"That's interesting – but what should I say in front of the camera?"

"Why not just tell everyone what you told me and talk about your school?" Zach suggested.

"Yes, thanks. I'll try my best."

"Zach, we are ready when you are," Muir called, once the whole group had assembled.

Cait clapped and cheered as Zach took his place in front of the camera. She thought him pleasing on the eye and he had been sweet to her since she had arrived. He told the group how he had grown up without a father. The occupants of the room listened with compassion for this young man who clearly adored his mother but had missed out on the love and attention of a male figure in his life. He talked about his passion for tennis, and how he had begun playing at the age of four after he found an old wooden racket in the attic that had once belonged to his father. It turned out that his dad had been a decent player in his youth and Zach had inherited a natural talent for hand-eye coordination. Now, at seventeen, he was preparing to head off to university in Southern California the following year to major in the sport, with the hope of turning professional one day.

As Zach moved clear of the camera and rejoined the group, everyone stood silent, as though in respect of what he had shared with them.

"USC in Downtown Los Angeles, eh? Good show. We will virtually be neighbours. We can hang out when you are there," Henry broke the silence.

"I have a feeling I won't have much time for hanging out, unfortunately," Zach replied. He tried not to laugh, thinking that he could not imagine anything worse.

"You were wonderful. I'm sorry about your dad," Cait said and gently touched Zach's arm.

"Thanks, I was just speaking from the heart. It was a long time ago and it felt the right moment to share it."

"It never gets any easier, though. My parents and I had to leave my grandparents in Hong Kong. We miss them so much. Who knows, if I win the money, I might be able to get them here," Cait said. "Here goes. Looks like it's my turn." Muir caught her eye.

"Knock 'em dead."

"I hope not."

Cait stood for a few seconds and stared into the camera. She closed her eyes, placed her hands in a prayer position on her chest and gave a small bow into the lens. "*Ni hao, wo jiao Kaite, we zhu zai niuyue,*" flowed effortlessly from her lips, before she translated the words to English. She told the captivated group that she had said hello in Chinese, that her name was Cait and that she lived in New York.

Over her initial fear, she slowly began to relax and settled into the story of how she was offered the chance to study ballet in New York and that her parents had to sell their home in Hong Kong to make the trip. Unfortunately, the funds were not available to allow her grandparents to travel to the United States with them and Cait had vowed to make enough money to bring the whole family together again one day. She knew she wasn't as brave as many people her age, but if it meant overcoming her fears to enter Hacker Hall and win the money to reunite her family, then that was what she was going to do.

"Fabulous," Zach said. "You didn't say you could speak Chinese."

"I'm not entirely fluent, but I know enough to get by. Sadly, I don't speak it enough here to improve."

"Nice job, Cait. Very well done," Muir congratulated Cait as he walked towards them. "Now, before we finish up, I would like to congratulate you all on your efforts here today. It has been a successful afternoon, and having met you all, I know wholeheartedly that Max and I have chosen the right five people for the show. Max and my assistant, Carol, are going to escort you to your hotel for the night. There are taxis waiting outside. Sadly, I am unable to join you tonight, but I will meet you back here tomorrow at ten o'clock. It will not be a long morning. We must sit down with the lawyers to complete consent forms and go over all the insurance details. Then, I thought we would round up with a slideshow that Gil has put together of Hacker Hall. It will give you all a thorough feel for the place in advance. So, please be assured that everything for your stay is taken care of at the hotel. When you dine tonight and have breakfast in the morning, it will go onto the studio account and taxis will collect you at nine forty-five. I wish you a comfortable night and will see you all tomorrow."

A round of applause rang out, with words of thanks given to Muir, Max and the crew.

"I'll certainly have a comfortable night. Father has upgraded my room to a suite. You are all welcome to join me for a little partying," Henry told everyone.

"I'm not staying at the hotel, but thanks anyway." Cait said politely. "I had better be getting home. I will see you all tomorrow." She knew she had a free period so missing school for a couple of hours was no problem.

"I'll walk down with you."

"Sorry, Zach, would you mind waiting back a moment? There is something I wish to talk to you about," Muir interrupted.

"It's okay, Zach. You talk to Mr Mason. I will see you in the morning."

As the group began to disperse and head for the studio exit, Muir, Max and Zach were left alone.

"Is everything all right, Mr Mason?" Zach asked, nervously.

"Oh yes, I just wanted to ask a small favour. I am rather concerned about Frankie. We can't fathom why she turned up alone today. We assumed she was travelling with her mother. I wonder if we could ask you to keep a close eye on her. A young girl her age should not be on her own. Carol has spoken to the hotel and they have put her in the room next to yours. Could you please make sure she is accompanied to dinner and breakfast and help her with anything she needs? I hate to impose but we would feel much happier."

"Sure, Mr Mason. No problem. It will be my pleasure. If you'll both excuse me, I had better run and catch up with her. See you tomorrow."

"Thank you. See you tomorrow," Muir said, as Zach ran out the door. "What a smashing young man. He will go far. You had better catch up with them, too, Max. Have a good evening."

"You too, Muir. See you in the morning."

SEVEN

FINAL PREPARATIONS

*O*n the morning of the 29th, everyone gathered back at the studio, having been transported by the famous New York Yellow Cab Company, with the exception of Cait, who made the short walk south from her parent's apartment in Harlem.

Everyone was in good spirits and chatted as if they had known each other for years. Mrs Carney stayed behind at the hotel to wait until Breena returned from the studio. The previous day had been too full-on for her. She was exhausted and wanted to rest before the flight back to Florida.

Henry was his usual bolshy self and boasted about how incredible his hotel suite had been. He also wondered why he had not seen any of the other contestants at dinner the evening before. Unbeknown to him, they had all chosen to take room service through fear of bumping into him. Zach had invited Frankie to eat with him in his room and they had watched movies and talked about their lives growing up in Pennsylvania.

Carol had returned to her apartment once she had helped everyone check-in and Max had eaten at a small Italian deli two blocks away, hoping to avoid seeing anyone at the hotel. He had thought about calling Imogen to fill her in on how the day had gone but decided to wait until all the contestants had gone home. Then, he would think about where he would spend the next two weeks until the show.

"Good morning, everyone. I hope you enjoyed your overnight stay," Muir greeted them as Carol escorted them into the boardroom once again.

"May I have a private word, please, Mr Mason?" Zach asked.

"Yes, of course. Come to my office. Please excuse us for a minute or two," Muir told the group.

"I spent some time with Frankie last night and asked how she had been able to travel alone. I don't want to get her into trouble, but it seems she never had any intention of bringing her mother. She told her she was going on a school trip to New York. Her mother left her at her friend's house, where they pretended to go into school to make the trip. Then she got a taxi to the station and took the train here alone. Quite a plan, don't you think?"

"Indeed, I do, Zach. Thanks for letting me know. I had Carol try to call her mother, but we couldn't get in touch with her anyway. Did she give a reason for the deception?"

"No, nothing. She just said her mother could not find out she was going into the hall."

"Interesting. Well, I don't want to get her into trouble either. I'm sure she has her reasons and she is quite safe here. She is certainly a brave little cookie, but if she wants to appear on the show, she will have to get her mother's consent. I wonder if I could impose on you one more time."

"Of course, Mr Mason, anything."

"If I have a taxi take you both to the station, would you travel back to Pennsylvania with her and put her in a cab home at the other end?"

"Sure, no worries."

"Good, let's get back to the others and sort all the legal stuff."

Over the next hour, the network legal team went through permissions, consents and insurance. As all five candidates were under the age of eighteen, they needed to take legal documents back to their parents or guardians to sign, otherwise Muir would not risk them being on the show. All the children were confident there would be no problems getting the permission – Muir hoped they were right, especially in Frankie's case. Time was moving on quickly and he would have been hard pushed to find new contestants at such a late stage. Besides, he was happy with the current five and hoped, dearly, he would not have to replace anyone.

Pleased to have the formalities over with, the group followed Muir and Gil upstairs to a small, windowless room set out like an intimate cinema. It contained about twenty large armchairs in rows and one wall was filled with a large white screen.

"Make yourselves comfortable and my assistant will bring in some refreshments," Muir told them.

"It's a mini cinema. Cool!" said Breena. "Will you sit next to me, Frankie?"

"Sure."

"It's good to see the girls getting along. Shall we sit here?" Zach indicated to seats on the end of the second row.

"Yes, thanks," Cait replied. "I guess they are a similar age, so it makes sense. And being thrown into this situation, we all have a common interest."

"Well, I'm going to sit in the front row," Henry chipped in. "I don't want to miss anything. We have a cinema room like this at home, you know."

"Just sit down, Henry, and be quiet."

"Ooh, Zach, didn't realise you were in charge."

"He is not. But I am. So, please sit down; we are ready to get started," Muir cut in, sternly.

"No problem, Muir. I'm ready for this, although I bet it's pretty lame."

"I've told you, Henry, it's Mr Mason to you, and if you find the slideshow lame, you should have no trouble sitting through it. If, however, anyone else finds the slideshow disturbing, just pop outside to Carol and she will get you a drink of water. Now, if you are all ready, I will hand over to Gil."

The lights in the room dipped and the white screen sprang into life. Gil stood at the side of the room with his trusted laptop on a table in front of him.

"Okay, guys, it's been a busy day and a half here in New York and from what I have seen, the five of you are going to make the show a roaring success. Nonetheless, we decided it was only fair to give you a quick insight into what you can expect when you enter Hacker Hall. Obviously, we don't want to spoil all the fun as that would take the element of surprise from you and the audience, but it would be unfair of us to send you in blindly. So, for the next half an hour, I have put together a slideshow depicting some of the delights you will experience on the night. There are none of the special effects that we have added, just the hall in its bare state, as we found it when we visited. It will give you a last opportunity to pull out, should you wish to, before you get your final consent forms signed."

"No pulling out for me. How bad can it be?"

"Don't underestimate the place, Henry. It is full of surprises and it has a mind of its own. Now, shall we begin? If you have any questions, we can address them at the end."

The viewers watched with interest. As the first few pictures showed the outside of Hacker Hall, whispers and gasps spread between the children. Some out of recognition; most out of shock. *If the outside of the hall caused such a stir, how would they react on seeing the inside?* Muir thought to himself, as he watched each of the children attentively.

Gil gave a knowledgeable account of what the children were looking at. He tried to give them a feel for the place based on his own experience, and all too quickly his pictures moved onto the inside of the hall. The gasps grew louder, as the slides showed them around, room to room. Soon the whispers stopped and the whole room sat in a stupefied silence. Cait covered her eyes several times, leaning towards Zach for solace. Henry sat with his mouth open, his bottom jaw almost on his chest. Breena was thankful her grandmother had not been there to witness what they were seeing, as she feared she would stop her taking part. Even Muir and Max felt slightly overwhelmed at once again witnessing the vile, appalling scenes that they had witnessed only weeks before.

When the screen went blank and Gil closed his laptop lid, you could have heard a ghost hovering overhead. Cait opened her eyes and even Henry was speechless for once in his life. One bonus, Muir noted, was that at least none of the children had left the room. He was worried, though, as to how Cait and the younger girls would manage.

"Thank you, Gil. Let's get the lights back up, then we can have a chat and answer any questions before we round things up." Muir left his seat and joined Gil at the front of the room.

"It is a pretty gruesome place. Do you think it was that awful when patients lived there?" Breena asked.

"I'm sure it was worse. We can only imagine what it must have been like to be an inmate," Muir replied.

"Do you have any idea how many rooms there are for us to explore? And can we go anywhere?"

"If you count all the individual cells in the basement and the stairwells, there are just over sixty rooms. You can go wherever you like with the exception of the doctors' office, which we will be turning into the control room for the show. It will be locked anyway and Max will be the only person permitted to enter it," Gil answered Zach's question.

"God, it will take forever to search that many rooms," Henry grumbled.

"Hopefully, with five of you, you will cover them all within a few hours," said Muir.

"So, how long will the show last?"

"We have airtime of up to five hours, Breena. If we wrap things up quicker, we can schedule a fill-in programme."

"Did anyone see the white circles in some of the pictures?" Frankie asked.

"No," came a group answer.

"Really? They looked like round balls of floating light. They were faint, but I saw them in quite a few of the photos."

"Actually, now you say so, I did notice something," Zach added. "It was like a flash of lightning through one of the shots."

"Ooh, I know what they are!" Breena seemed excited. "They are called 'orbs' – you see them in ghost-hunting shows all the time. It is believed they are ghostly apparitions, showing the spirits of dead people."

"Cool," Henry said. "So, the place is haunted. This competition just got a whole lot more exciting."

"No, guys, stop! Those things are usually considered to be backscatter. Just dust particles picked up by the camera, which cannot be seen by the naked eye," Gil explained.

"Okay, don't spoil all the fun," Henry told him.

"Well, ghost hunters think they are real. And I do, too," Breena told everyone. "And I bet the audience will see them during the filming as well. This is going to be such fun. I'm not sure I can wait another two weeks!"

"I'm afraid you have to, but two weeks will pass quickly. There is still much planning and preparation to carry out," Muir said. "Now, if there are no more questions, I think you have trains and planes to catch."

Before the group went their separate ways, Muir told them all that his assistant, Carol, would send details on when to arrive at Hacker Hall, along with their travel and hotel information. He reminded them that the signed consent forms were required back seven days before the show aired and that he was pleased with how everything was coming together. He thanked the children for making the trip to New York and expressed how happy he was that they had all entered the competition. He ended by telling them that he believed the show would be a huge hit and was likely to be something that would be talked about for years to come.

The children chatted briefly before they exited the building. Henry left first, by limousine, which had been waiting to take him to the private airfield. Taxis were waiting: one to take Breena to the airport, via the hotel to collect her grandmother; the other to take Zach and Frankie to the station. Then, lastly, Cait left, walking slowly away from the building, waving at the taxis as they drove past.

"What a great bunch of kids," Muir expressed, as he watched them leave from his office window.

"They sure are. Henry is a cocky little whatsit, but they make a good mix," Max replied.

"I worry slightly about Cait. She is so fragile, but, as you say, the five of them make a good mix. Well, Max, we are almost there. Two weeks and we get this show on the road. What are your plans until then? You are welcome to stay here in New York at the hotel if you wish."

"Thanks, Muir. I may stay around for a few days and then head off. But don't fear, I will be in Pennsylvania in plenty of time. This show is all I have dreamed about for a long time."

"Hey, Imogen, guess who?"

"Max. How lovely to hear from you! Though I was rather hoping you had got trapped under a rock or something."

"Always the joker. I've missed you and thought I would fill you in on how things have gone here in the Big Apple."

"Well, I haven't missed you, but I guess you had better tell me about it."

"The kids seem all right. Not that I know or care about that really, but Muir seems pleased with them. There is one who is a rich, brattish moron. Hopefully, he will get his comeuppance. The rest seem fine, though."

"The same could be said of you, don't you think?"

"Bitchiness does not become you, dear Imogen. How is Daddy's campaign going? I hope he is getting plenty of votes."

"Touché, Max. So, when can I expect the pleasure of your company?"

"I am going to stay here for a few days – maybe a week. I want to be around the studio in case Muir needs me. I guess I will be with you by about the 9th or 10th. Any chance you can put me up until the crew arrive?"

"Not a hope in hell. Why don't you stay at the hall? It is going to make your fortune, after all."

"Not likely, but don't you worry about me. I always end up on my feet. Just remember; if Daddy wants to end up on his feet, too, you will cooperate. Together, my dear, we will make the House of a Hundred Doors a huge success for everyone concerned. Take care now, Imogen, and I'll see you in about ten days."

BASEMENT

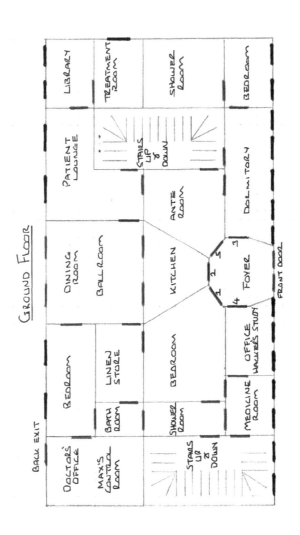

GROUND FLOOR

First Floor

STORE

DORMITORY

BATH ROOM

MEDICINE ROOM

PATIENT SITTING ROOM

STAIRS UP & DOWN

FIRE ESCAPE

DOCTOR'S BEDROOM

DOCTOR'S BATH

CORRIDOR

DORMITORY

DOCTOR'S BEDROOM

DOCTOR'S BATH

VAULTED FOYER

DOCTOR'S KITCHEN

DOCTOR'S LOUNGE

STAIRS DOWN

NURSE'S BEDROOM

NURSE'S BATHROOM

MEDICINE STORE

DOCTORS' DINING ROOM

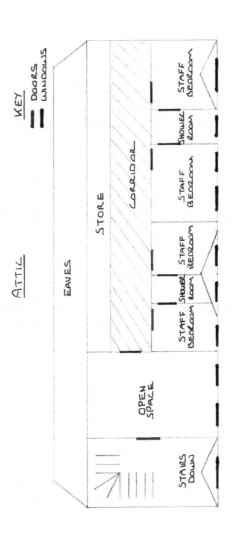

PART TWO

THE SHOW

EIGHT

RETURN TO HACKERS HOLLOW

It had been barely five months since Maximillion Crooked had walked into the bar in Pennsylvania and met Imogen Hackerton. Yet it felt like an eternity. He believed that he had a destiny and the wait was almost over. Within the next few hours, his plan would come to fruition and his dreams would come true. It had been a relatively simple plan, once he had the TV network on board, but there was still a fair way to go. However, if everything played out as he hoped it would, Max would leave Pennsylvania an incredibly rich man.

Muir had just left the trailer where Max sat, preparing for his performance of a lifetime. As he looked down at the large briefcase on the table in front of him, he began, for the first time, to feel a pang of nerves.

"So, here it is, Max. For your eyes only, until one of the lucky five relieve us of it." Muir had told him as he'd entered the trailer and placed the case down.

"Crikey, this is really happening, isn't it? Can I open it?"

"Sure, take a look – it's all there. Ready for you to hide in the hall wherever you choose." Max remembered Muir's exact words.

He had then slowly opened the two fastenings on the side of the case and looked inside. "My God! One hundred thousand dollars. It's beautiful, Muir. I have never seen that much money in my life. This night is going to make someone very happy. Very happy, indeed."

Max was, of course, referring to himself rather than one of the five contestants. His luck had changed the day he met Imogen, and now he was on the cusp of making the life for himself that he had always believed he deserved.

Of course, there was always a chance that the other larger sum of money may not exist in Hacker Hall. And if it did, anything could have happened to it over the last one hundred years. Still, Max had full faith in Imogen's story. He had to trust that everything she'd told him was true and that the money could be found within the walls of the House of a Hundred Doors.

Suddenly, pushing away his nerves, it dawned on Max that if the Hacker millions did not exist or could not be found, he had a case of one hundred thousand dollars in his possession and he would ensure that no one found it but him. The show would go ahead in a few hours' time and Max smiled to himself knowing that, one way or another, he would walk away at the end of the day much richer than he had begun it.

"Knock, knock!" Max recognised Imogen's voice, as the knocking on the door interrupted his thoughts.

"Come in, my lovely."

Max had arrived back in Pennsylvania the day before and had called Imogen the moment he got into town. He had tried his hardest to bully her into giving him a place to stay for the night, but she had stood her ground and insisted that her parents were not in a position to have house guests. He had not wanted to spend the money, but with no alternative had checked himself into the Hackers Hollow Guesthouse. He knew that Muir's assistant had booked a room for him there the night after the show, so he took it upon himself to check-in twenty-four hours early and hoped that Muir would be prepared to foot the bill for the additional night.

The television network production convoy had arrived in town earlier that morning, sending the whole town into a frenzy of excitement. The upcoming show had become common knowledge the day after all the contestants had left New York after their screen tests. Muir had Gil and the team put together a television advertisement that went live across the eastern states and the results were immediate. The phones started to ring and the live audience tickets for the show sold out within two days.

A certain number of seats had been kept back to be sold purely to residents of the town. Those who were not fortunate enough to purchase a ticket were planning on waiting outside the hall for any glimpse they could get. The rest would watch the show live, along with the rest of the nation.

Some of the residents seemed to be against the publicity and mayhem that was about to hit their town. Most, however, were intrigued and happy that their little town was getting some recognition. The townspeople had always been interested in Hacker Hall and hoped that, once and for all, some of its ghosts would be laid to rest.

"You are here, then?" Imogen stated, as she entered the state-of-the-art caravan.

"You bet I am. Where else would I be? You knew that once the TV network were on board, I would go ahead with the plan. It's good to see you. Hey, come and look at this. Muir just dropped it off." Max bent down to pick up the briefcase. "One hundred thousand dollars," he said, as he opened the case for the second time. "Isn't it fantastic?"

"I guess so. I just hope that when the show is over tonight, you will be satisfied and get out of our lives, once and for all."

"A promise is a promise, Imogen."

"Good. Make sure you keep it. Hey, what will you do if Hacker's fortune is not found? Have you thought about that?" she asked.

"Sure, the thought entered my head, when you interrupted me just now."

"Well, will you still leave?"

"Of course. After all, if your great-great-great granddaddy's money is not in there, I still have this lovely case full of loot. Not as much as I would have hoped for, but hey, beggars can't be choosers. It is still a pretty nice amount of money for very little work."

"My God. You really are the worst kind of person ever placed on this earth. One day, Maximillion Crooked, you will get your comeuppance and you will thoroughly deserve everything that is coming your way."

"Yeah, yeah, I know, but at least I will go out having a good time – whenever it happens."

"If the universe has anything to do with it, it will be sooner rather than later."

"So funny, Imogen. Tell me, did you actually come in for a reason or because you just couldn't keep away from me?" Max asked, with an air of sarcasm.

"Keeping away is the one thing I *can* do, Max. I just wanted to say good luck for the show and I hope that you get what you deserve."

"Oh, I will, Imogen. I will. Now, run along and let me prepare myself. I have to think about where I am going to hide all this lovely money. Oh no, wait a second. I don't have to hide it at all. Just keep it *close by*. Ooh, isn't this a wonderful world?"

"Whatever you say, Max. Just remember that they are only children in there. Be nice to them," Imogen pleaded.

"Where are you going to watch the show?" Max asked.

"I have no intention of watching you manipulate everyone and carry out your sordid plan. I am going to wait in the production trailer with Gil."

"I should have guessed you two lovebirds would hook up once he came into town."

"It's nothing like that. Think what you like, though, I really don't care," Imogen said, as she walked to the door.

"I always do, and Imogen, thanks for having a rich great-great-great-granddaddy."

Imogen slammed the door of Max's trailer as she departed and left him alone, once again. Four hours to go before the start of the show. Max picked up the briefcase and looked around the beautifully equipped caravan for somewhere to hide it until it was needed. There was little chance of anyone taking the money or even knowing it was there – but one could never be too careful.

He found a sliding door, concealing a large compartment, behind one of the cushions that made up a sofa at one end of the trailer and carefully placed the briefcase inside. The moment he placed the cushions back in place, a shrill buzzing sound took Max by surprise.

"What the hell?" he mumbled, as he stood and looked around for the cause of the noise. It took just a moment for him to see a red light flashing on the desk in the corner.

"Ah, the Bat Phone," he said to himself as he flicked the switch. It was an intercom system set up between all the other trailers, so everyone connected with the show could speak to each other. It was the first time since Max had arrived that it had buzzed and it had caught him off guard.

"Hello?"

"Max, hi. Gil here. It's about time we got into the hall for the last sound and camera check. We only have two hours left until the live audience are allowed in the gates, so we had better get it done now. We want to keep our movements outside the hall to a minimum once people start to enter and take their seats."

"Sure, Gil, I will meet you at the rear door in a couple of minutes."

Max grabbed his jacket and the keys to the trailer and made his exit, locking the door behind him.

The same keyring contained the keys to the front door and the door at the back of Hacker Hall, which gave Max access to the old doctors' meeting room, where he would spend the duration of the show.

"Evening, Gil," Max said, as they met outside the door.

"Evening, Max. Almost ready?"

"Yeah. When we are finished here, I shall have a bite to eat. Then off to make-up and away we go."

"Well, let's get inside and I will show you the ropes."

Max unlocked the door and the two men entered. The room in no way resembled the space that Max had seen on his last visit to the hall.

"Wow! I have never seen so much equipment. Did you guys bring all this stuff down from the studio?"

"Sure did, Max. The team and I have worked flat out since the second we arrived early this morning. Setting everything up and placing the cameras and mics in every room."

"Good job."

"Thanks. It's all in a day's work. Now, let me go over what we have here. Firstly, you will see that you have seven screens. Five to follow each of the kids, so you can see what they are doing whatever room they are in. One to show the rest of the rooms that are not in use. That screen is split into six so you can see multiple rooms and it rotates throughout the whole building, changing every thirty seconds. And the last one is to show you a floor plan of the four floors, in case you forget the layout and where the individual rooms are."

"Looks complicated. Do you have the same equipment in the production van?"

"Afraid not. In that respect, you are on your own. The team and I did a check of the electric supply when we were last here. There is just not enough power, so we brought generators from New York, but they only provide enough power for one set of equipment. I can, however, control the main power supply from my end, too. I will turn everything on fifteen minutes before we go live, and in the event an emergency, I also have the ability to cut everything and shut down the show – but that would only ever be on Muir's orders, of course. You will know if that occurs as you will lose all sound and visuals in here. In the event of that happening, leave via the back door and head round to the front of the hall. An automatic cue card will inform you what to tell the audience. We will do the rest. We have the emergency services on hand. They will then enter the hall, locate the children and get them out."

"You make it sound pretty scary." Max looked worried.

"No, not at all. I just have to make you aware of the worst-case scenario."

"I know. What can the worst-case scenario be, anyway? Anyone would think the Bogeyman is going to show himself," Max said, trying to make light of the situation.

"No chance of that. I have it on good authority that it's his night off," Gil joked. "But do remember, you will witness many special effects that we have put in place, so be prepared for a shock or two. Now, let's go over the rest of this stuff. You will see at the bottom of each screen: a camera number, a floor number and a room name. If you want to look more closely at any images of the rooms, type the camera number into the keyboard and you can zoom in and out. Just remember to press the escape button to return you to the normal camera angle."

"That seems easy enough," Max commented, thinking that it would be a very useful tool to keep a close eye on what the children were doing. Especially when the money was found. "Anything else?"

"Yes, almost there. You will see, under each of the screens that show the children, a button and two switches. The button is to control the camera. You can use it to shut off the camera in the particular room they are in, should you need to. And the first switch is for you to speak directly to the children. Like an intercom."

"Cool. But surely, we don't want the audience to hear everything I am saying. Shouldn't they be focused on what the contestants are doing?" Max wondered.

"Quite right. You can turn off the third switch to cut off the external mic for the relevant room. Outside, the audience only have five large video screens. One to watch each of the children as they move around the hall. They will be able to hear what each of the children say, if they say anything, on their individual screens. Although they won't be able to hear what you say to the children if they speak to you. Sort of like a two-way PA system between you and the children, but only one-way between the children and the audience."

"Great idea. But surely the audience might get rather confused if they can hear all five children speaking at once."

"We realised that, too. We doubt the children will all talk constantly at the same time so the audience will hear them as they do, however if more than one of them speaks, the outside mics will only allow one voice to be heard, alternating through until only one of them is speaking again."

"Wow! I bet that took some sorting?"

"Nothing too complicated with the wonders of technology we have these days. Okay, lastly, this camera here." Gil pointed to a small camera in the corner of the room, "That is your live feed to the outside, for when you need to speak to the audience. Obviously, they can see what the contestants are always up to as long as you keep the cameras on, but it is also your job to show your charming self to them on occasion throughout the show to keep them updated and amused. When you use it, your face will appear in the corner of one of the five external screens, and you can turn it on and off as you wish."

"Keep them amused. That I can do. Anything else?"

"Yes, just one more thing. Keep the internal door into the hall locked at all times. We do not want the children wandering in here at any time."

"Not a problem. You can count on me, Gil. Hang on, if you don't have access to screens in the production trailer, how are you going to watch the show?"

"I won't be able to see what is happening, but I can hear everything clearly, so I will know everyone's move. If I need to, I can go to Muir's trailer and watch on his TV, or even head outside to watch on the giant video screens."

"I don't think you had better do that, you might miss Imogen," Max told him.

"What do you mean?"

"She told me that she does not want to watch the show, so she is planning to come to the production trailer and spend the evening with you. You're a lucky man, Gil."

"Maybe she will, but there is nothing going on, Max. We are here to make a TV show, remember."

"I know. Just teasing."

"Well, don't let Imogen hear you. She is a decent woman and I don't want you to go upsetting her."

"Yeah, yeah. Message received loud and clear. Now, let's get this place locked up. I need some supper before I dress for the show."

"Sure thing, Max, and remember you can buzz me if you need anything once we air. There is the same intercom connection as you have in your trailer," Gil said, pointing to a similar red button as the one Max had earlier referred to as the Bat Phone.

"Will do, Gil, and thanks for everything, mate."

"No problem, Max."

Gil left the production room via the back door, ahead of Max, and thought for a moment that the man had actually seemed human. He was clearly excited now the time had come for his show to take place. Gil wondered, for a brief second, if he had misjudged him on their previous meetings.

Max locked the door behind him and returned to his own caravan. Gil had shown him the ropes and he now had a good handle on how the evening was going to play out. He planned to head over to the cafeteria and eat the meal he had requested. Then, he would retrieve the one hundred thousand dollars from his trailer and place it in the cupboard in the production room. Max smiled to himself. Yes, he was happy. Yes, he was excited. And yes, before the night was over, he would be a very rich man.

As Max tucked into his plate of rare steak with chips and salad, the five contestants and their families arrived in taxis from the guesthouse. Muir's assistant, Carol, had requested that they all be allowed to check-in early in order to rest before the events of the evening.

Henry had once again flown in from California on his father's private jet, accompanied this time by his mother, Madeline. Breena had flown in with her grandmother, Mrs Carney, from Florida and Cait had taken the Amtrak from New York with her parents.

Zach and Frankie, being local, had not required hotel rooms and had made the short journey across town. Zach had been collected from his house by taxi, where his mother promised to watch every second of the show. Frankie had been collected from her friend Tilly's house, where she had told her mother she was staying for the weekend.

Muir and Gil rushed out to meet them all as they gathered on the path in front of the main entrance.

"My God, what an awful place. As old and gloomy as the hotel room we have just left."

"Mrs Fortune, I presume?" Muir extended his hand, which was duly ignored by the woman standing before him in an ankle-length fur coat.

"Mother, this is Mr Mason, the owner of the network that is putting on the show," Henry told her. Much to Muir's delight, the boy had remembered not to call him by his Christian name.

"Yes, I guessed it was. Johnson described you perfectly," she replied, looking Muir up and down. "And who is this charming young man?"

"Hello, I'm Gil," he said, stepping forward, without attempting to shake Mrs Fortune's hand.

"And what do you do?"

"I head up the production team that have—"

"That's lovely, dear. Would you mind bringing me a cup of coffee?" she interrupted Gil, who threw Muir a glance that told a thousand words. Madeline Fortune was going to be hard work and they could now see where Henry had inherited his arrogance from.

"Mr Mason, Gil. How wonderful to see you both again. Gosh, this is exciting, isn't it?" Zach moved in next to Henry and his mother to break up the awkward conversation.

"Zach, my boy. Great to see you. We are so glad you are here," Muir said, warmly, shaking his hand.

"Thank you, Sir. I'm delighted to be here."

"Zach!" came a voice from behind him that he recognised straightaway.

"Cait, it's so good to see you and that we are all here together."

"Zach, please meet my parents," Cait said. "Mum, Dad, this is Zach. And this is Mr Mason, who has kindly allowed me to be on the show, and this is Gil."

There was a lot of chatting, hugging and shaking hands as introductions and rekindling of friendships occurred.

Frankie, Breena and Mrs Carney joined the group and the conversations continued, as if they were old friends, with the exception of Mrs Fortune, who seemed very uneasy. Muir wondered if she would make it through the night.

"Has anyone seen Imogen?" Muir asked. "I would like you all to meet her as she was not in New York with us."

"After I left Max, I looked for her and the team reckon she popped home. She wanted to eat and get changed. She promised to be back before we go live," Gil told him.

"No problem. We'll catch up with her later then," Muir said. "Okay, let's get everyone sorted. If you would like to follow me around to the back of the hall, we will get you kids into make-up and the rest of you into the comfort of my trailer, where you can relax until you take your seats. Two hours to go, guys. I hope you are ready for this."

"I'm still waiting for a coffee," was all Mrs Fortune could say, as the group followed Muir and Gil to prepare for the show of their lives.

Imogen had driven herself back to her parent's house after she had spoken to Max in his trailer. The to-ing and fro-ing that they always shared when they spoke was exhausting for her. She knew it was only friendly banter for Max, but there were always the underlying tones of what he was really like and what he was actually up to.

From the day she had met him, she'd regretted ever mentioning Hacker Hall and her family connection with the place. Nevertheless, that was done, and now, at this late stage, she knew there was nothing she could do to stop him carrying out his plan.

"So, this programme is definitely going ahead then?" Emerson Hackerton asked his daughter, when he arrived home after a long day of campaigning.

"Yes, Daddy, it sure is. It is very good of you to give your permission."

"Well, I'm not sure why, but I could see it meant a lot to you. So, anything to please my little Imogen. Are you sure that Mr Mason and his colleagues still don't know who owns the house?" Emerson questioned.

"I'm sure, Daddy. They have only dealt with the man from the council offices in Williamsport and he has remained incredibly tight-lipped. Nothing for you to worry about."

"That's good. Now, dinnertime."

"Will you not come back to the hall with me and watch the show as it happens live?"

"I don't think so, Imogen. It's been a long day and that sort of publicity, I do not need. Will you stay for dinner with your mother and I before you head back?"

"Yes, thank you, Daddy, I think I have time," Imogen said, looking at her watch. "I will just grab a quick shower and be back down to join you both. I have an hour before it all kicks off."

Max had finished his pre-show dinner, retrieved the case of prize money from his trailer, taken it into the production room through the back door and carefully placed it in the cupboard, under where all the equipment had been set up. He placed a blanket over the top of it to conceal it from view, should anyone happen to get into the room. He was very happy with how things were going as he left and locked the door behind him.

"Ah, Max, how are you doing?" Muir appeared in the now-dark grounds.

"Crikey, Muir, give a fella a heart attack, why don't you?"

"Sorry. A bit jumpy, are we? Nerves getting to you and all that," Muir teased.

"You just took me by surprise, that's all."

"The gates opened some time ago so the live audience are flooding in and taking their seats already. It's almost time, Max. Have you seen the kids yet? They have just finished in make-up," Muir asked.

"No, I have been busy. Do they really need make-up?"

"Not really. It's just a little theatrical matt foundation, so their faces do not look too shiny under the lights when the cameras are on them."

"I guess I'd better get some of that. I'm heading that way now."

"Good. I am going to head back to my trailer so I can escort the children's families to their seats. Well, Max, it's almost time for you to make your debut as a television presenter. I want to wish you the best of luck and I'll see you on the other side."

Muir vanished into the darkness as quickly as he had appeared, leaving Max to walk alone to the make-up trailer. His face was made up in a neutral manner, his hair was brushed, backcombed and sprayed, and before long he headed to his trailer for the final wait.

When Max arrived at his trailer, he found a suit-carrier bag hanging on the outside of the door. He knew it was his outfit for the show and had been left by the costume department. He took it inside and laid the contents out on the sofa.

Navy dress trousers, a starched white shirt and navy bow tie, and, finally, a bespoke, gold lamé jacket. Max dressed and stood looking at himself in the full-length mirror on the front of one of the cupboards. He had never considered himself an overly handsome man, but good-looking enough to attract the ladies. When they really got to know him, they always said his true personality shone through. He had never quite understood that. He was always honest with the women he met. He had never hidden the fact that money was the most important thing in his life. Even with Imogen, he had never pretended to be anything other than the man that he was.

None of that mattered anymore. From now on, he would forget women and live life to the full on his own, on his terms, with no one telling him what to do or getting in his way. He had a new life ahead of him. A very rich one and he was going to enjoy every second of it.

A buzzing sound cut into his thoughts. Max pressed the button to hear Gil's voice. "Ten minutes until we go live, Max. Are you ready?"

"As ready as I will ever be."

"Good luck then, Max. Break a leg."

"I hope not," Max replied, as he took a last glance in the mirror. "This is it," he said to his reflection. "Show time!"

Nine

SHOW TIME

"Okay, Max, let's go," Max heard Gil's voice through the small listening device in his left ear. "When the lights go out, and the front of the hall and the grounds fall into complete darkness, move onto the spot marked outside the main entrance. A bright spotlight will shine all around you – and you will be on, live to the audience gathered and the rest of America."

Max stood at the corner of the building, waiting for his moment. A few deep breaths and some gentle words of encouragement to himself, and suddenly the grounds fell into darkness. Max walked quickly to the exact spot he knew had been marked earlier, took one last breath and – pow! Bright lights illuminated the area around him and the audience erupted into rapturous applause.

"A very good evening, ladies and gentlemen, boys and girls. It is a chilly night here on Friday 13th of May and I welcome you all to Pennsylvania." Max lingered over the words as he read from the autocue prompter in front of him. "We are gathered here at this ancient gothic mansion for an incredibly special, one-off show where five extraordinary children are waiting in the wings to enter the house. Once inside, they will search the building, and by the end of the night, one of them will emerge as our winner, having located the prize bag of one hundred thousand dollars!" Max shouted, as gasps of "Wow!" and "Woohoo!" rang out from the audience. "Now, we cannot promise you Freddie Kruger, but we can promise you thrills, chills and even bumps in the night as you witness the horrors that this decaying domicile has to offer. Remember, once inside, nothing is as it seems, yet everything seems to be something. My name is Maximillion Crooked and I will be your host for the duration of the evening. So, without further ado, let's bring out the children and get the show underway."

Another round of clapping exploded from the hands of the live audience as lights around the grounds began to flash. Then, a few seconds later, the five children ran from their waiting place to meet Max in front of the hall. Shouts and cheers rang out and the large video screens sprang into life – each one showing the individual faces of the children.

"Right then, everybody, allow me to introduce to you our five carefully chosen contestants. The lucky five were picked from thousands of entrants to be here to entertain you tonight. First up, we have Zach. Come forward, Zach, and introduce yourself to everyone."

"Good evening, ladies and gentlemen. My name is Zach Hamilton. I am seventeen years old and I live right here in Hackers Hollow."

Screams and shouts of enthusiasm came from the voices of the audience and Max called Cait to come forward next.

"*Ni hao.* Hello, my name is Cait and I am sixteen years old. I live in New York with my parents and I am on a ballet scholarship at The New York Performing Arts Academy."

"Thank you, Cait. It sounds as if the audience appreciate you from the applause. Next up, we have another young man. Henry, come forward and tell us about yourself."

"Thanks, Max. Hi everyone, I'm Henry Fortune, all the way from sunny California. My father is also a television man, so I am used to this sort of environment. I am here to tell you all that, for me, second place is not an option. I am here to win."

Booing and shouting rang out from the audience. Max and the other children smiled to themselves. It amused them to see that the audience already had a handle on Henry at such an early stage. They had immediately made him the villain and his popularity was going to be low.

Max called Breena to introduce herself next, which she did beautifully, and after the negativity towards Henry she got the audience on her side straightaway. She said how she had a great love for horror, which they seemed to appreciate, bearing in mind where they were.

Lastly, Max called Frankie to the front.

"Good evening, everyone, my name is Frankie Hatter and I am twelve years old. Like Zach, I am a local girl, but unlike the other contestants I have been in the hall before. The locals have always said it is haunted and I would like to prove to you all that it isn't."

"Thank you for that, Frankie." Max took centre stage once more. "And thank you to all five of you for being here tonight and showing how brave you are to be entering this old and very spooky building, haunted or not. So, there it is, ladies and gentlemen. You have met our five intrepid children who are all here on the most amazing mission. In a few moments from now, when we enter the hall, you will be able to follow their escapades on the video screens. And, as they meander their way around inside, you can make up your own minds as to whom you are routing for. Then, wait with bated breath over the next few hours to find out which of them will be victorious and walk away with the coveted one hundred thousand dollar prize. So, there you have it. Sit back, relax and come with me, as we watch Zach, Cait, Henry, Breena and Frankie run wild and explore the House of a Hundred Doors."

Once again, the lights around the grounds flashed in bright colours and the five giant video screens went blank. Max and the five children walked towards the main entrance. They mounted the small flight of stairs that led up to the veranda, which had been securely mended since Muir had fallen through it on the first visit to the hall. All six turned to face the audience, waved for a moment, then disappeared inside Hacker Hall – the House of a Hundred Doors – to commence the search.

"Is dinner ready yet, Daddy?" Imogen asked, when she returned to the drawing room, having showered and changed into a casual pair of trousers and cashmere sweater.

"Not quite, sweetheart. Your mother gave the cook the night off and you know the kitchen is not her favourite place."

"I hope she hurries up or I will miss the start of the show."

"Just relax and have a drink with me. She won't be much longer. I didn't think you wanted to watch anyway."

"Oh, I am not going to watch, but Mr Mason and Gil will be wondering where I am."

"Ah yes, the young man you mentioned a while back. I get the impression you rather like him."

"Oh, Daddy. He is just a nice man, and he was very sweet and helpful to me when he was last in Hackers Hollow."

"Sounds as though you are smitten to me, my darling."

"Don't tease. Besides, he lives in New York and will be heading back there tomorrow once the show is over. So, even if I did feel something, and I'm not saying I do, nothing could come of it with him living that far away."

"Nonsense, Imogen. Your mother and I lived in different states when we first met. If something is meant to be, you will both find a way to make it work. Anyhow, New York is hardly the other side of the world. It is only two hours from here, you know."

"I know. We will have to wait and see. Now, let's change the subject. Are you and Mummy going to watch the show on television?"

"I don't reckon so. You know your mother is not fond of anything to do with the place and I don't want to upset her nerves."

"Yes, you are right. I will let you know how it goes tomorrow."

At that moment, Imogen and Emerson heard a call from the kitchen. They made their way to the dining room, having been informed their evening meal was ready.

Imogen enjoyed dinner with her parents before she checked her watch and made her exit, knowing that as she headed back to Hacker Hall, the live show had already started.

Having ushered the children inside Hacker Hall, Max closed the door behind him. As he did so, the five large video screens in the grounds burst into life once again. They were on their way. The show had started; Max knew he had to be on his best behaviour for the sake of the viewers and play by the rules until his moment came, when Harrison Hacker's money was found. Once it was found, and in his possession, he would make the switch with the prize bag he had hidden in the control room. He had not considered that far ahead at this stage as he had no way of knowing how the events of the evening would play out. He just hoped that when the moment presented itself, he would know exactly what to do.

"Okay, ladies and gentlemen, here we go. You find us here in the entrance foyer of Hacker Hall. The first thing you will observe is that it is a bland, empty space. I wish we could bring the smell to you all, to add to the atmosphere, but you will have to take it from me; it is pretty foul in here. We are standing in an almost octagonal-shaped area that was the first glimpse anyone ever got of the inside of the hall. And, true to the name of the show, we begin with a series of five doors, all leading off to different parts of the hall. I have in my pocket five folded pieces of paper, each numbered one to five. Beginning with the youngest contestant, each will choose one piece of paper, enter into the bowels of the building and the competition will begin."

Zach, Cait, Henry, Breena and Frankie looked on nervously as Max briefly outlined to everyone watching that they could move around freely and search anywhere, but if they came across each other in their travels they were, under no circumstances, to assist each other. And once they had all entered their first doors and gone on their way, he would exit the front door, lock it behind him and head around the back of the building to the equipment room, from where he would control the show.

"Right, here goes," Max said, sensing the nervous energy in the room. He placed his hand in his pocket to retrieve the five pieces of numbered paper. "Frankie, you are our youngest contestant and therefore lucky enough to enter first. And of course, having been here before, you will no doubt recognise this room."

"Yes, Max, I do. It was a few years ago, but who could forget this place?" Frankie was already playing to the audience.

"Quite right. Now, Frankie, would you please take a piece of paper and tell everyone the number you have chosen?"

"Hooray!" she shouted. "It's three. My lucky number."

"Well, that's a good start. There you are, Frankie. You can see the first door on the right is number three. Would you like to enter now and begin your search?" Max asked.

"Sure will, Max. Bye, everyone, and good luck." Frankie opened the door, walked through and disappeared into her first room.

"Super job, Frankie, and best of luck," Max said. "Now, next up, Breena. Come and choose your number."

"Gosh, Max. I can hardly contain my excitement! I have waited for this for so long," Breena told the audience as she unravelled the paper she had picked. "It's number two!"

"Good job, that is the door directly in front of us. The middle one of the five. Off you go, Breena," Max told her.

"Thanks. Here I go. Wish me luck."

"I don't think you will need it," Max said, as she waved and went through the central door in the room. "Okay, it's the turn of our first, and very self-assured, young man, Henry. Come on, Henry, take your number."

Henry took another of the three remaining pieces of paper, opened its folds and held it up towards the camera in the corner of the room.

"Yes! It's number one. That is a good omen. Number one for the number one. I told you I was going to win," Henry shouted, as he moved to the door that stood between the centre one and the one on the far left. "See you all when I have the prize money with me!" He entered the door completely unaware of the boos from the audience outside.

"Well, there goes a very confident contestant. Let's wait and see if he is as successful as he believes. Now, just two left. Cait, it's your turn." Max watched as a look of horror appeared on Cait's face.

Zach picked up on her fear, too. "Is everything all right, Cait?" he asked.

"Oh no, Zach. A terrible chill just ran over me and I am feeling quite sick. I really don't think I can go through with it. I knew it would be tough, but I never imagined I would feel this scared."

"Oh dear, ladies and gentlemen. It looks as though we may have our first contestant that wants out – even before entering the first room. What a shame," Max said.

"Hang on, Max," Zach spoke up. "Give me a moment. What are you so scared of, Cait?"

"Everything. What if the place is haunted? What if something happens to one of us?"

"Cait, the place is not haunted and nothing is going to happen. There are cameras everywhere. People are watching our every move. We will be perfectly safe."

"I know, Zach. But what if—?"

"No 'what ifs'. Just remind yourself why you are here. How good would it be to have your grandparents in New York with you? Your family would be complete again. They are routing for you and so am I. Come on; you can do this."

"Oh, Zach, I agree with everything you say, but I'm really frightened to go in there."

"How about we go in at the same time? We will open the remaining two pieces of paper to choose our doors and we will enter at exactly the same time. I know you can do this. What do you say?"

Max, Cait's parents and the whole of America watched, unable to move. A true gentleman had been born and he was showing Cait, and everyone, that he was very special. As they looked at each other, audiences believed they could be witnessing the start of a wonderful relationship and held their breaths, waiting for Cait's answer.

"Yes, Zach. You are right. I can do this." Cheers rang out from the watching audience. "Max, can we go in together?"

"I don't see why not; it will not alter how things work out. So, ladies and gentlemen, we have a 'yes'. Cait is going in and so is Zach," Max told the camera. "Come on, you two, choose your numbers." Max held out the final two pieces of paper. Cait took one and Zach, the other.

"I have number four," Cait said, quietly, still feeling rather nervous.

"And I have number five," Zach replied.

"Okay, here we go. Our last two contestants are about to start the game. Cait, you have the first door on the left and Zach, you have the door between the ones that Frankie and Breena entered. Are you both ready?"

Both Cait and Zach turned to face Max and nodded. Zach took hold of Cait's hand, kissed it and wished her good luck. The audience outside cheered and shouted cries of "Ahh!", happy with what they were seeing.

The pair stood in front of their respective doors and Zach counted down from three. On the count of one, they opened their doors and, a second later, were both gone.

"And there you have it, ladies and gentlemen. Our five contestants have entered the House of a Hundred Doors and our show is underway."

Max exited through the front door and off the veranda. "I will now make my way around to the back of the hall and into the control room, where you will hear me, on occasion, as I commentate on the night's proceedings. So, watch as the children search the hall, enjoy the thrills and chills, and I will see you again when one of them is victorious."

With that, Max vanished into the night to a round of applause. All he had to do now was to take his place in the small room at the back of the house and wait until one of the five children found the Hacker millions and handed it over.

Imogen arrived at Hacker Hall just in time to see Max run round the back and enter the production room to control the show. She did not call out. She knew he had the show to get on with and did not want to bother him or contend with another awkward conversation.

"Thank God, you've arrived. I was getting worried. Where have you been?" Gil asked, when she entered the trailer, where he was already listening to the show.

"I went home to have a shower and get changed. I didn't mean to be so long."

"Is everything all right? I thought you were sticking around the hall."

"I had intended to, but I didn't want to keep bumping into Max. So, I thought I would pop home for a while and clear my head," Imogen tried not to give too much away.

"Did he do something to upset you?"

"No, nothing really. I just knew he had a lot on his mind, so I wanted to leave him to it. I'm sorry I missed the children," she said, changing the subject. "I really wanted to meet them."

"Well, they are in the house now. They have all just entered their first rooms. Cait had a tiny wobble and we thought for a second she might not go through with it, but Zach talked her round. He's a good guy. I know I shouldn't have a favourite, but I wouldn't mind if he won."

"Good job he was able to get through to her. Let's hope she will be okay inside."

"I'm sure she will be fine once she gets into the swing of it. She has the motivation of bringing her grandparents to America, so I guess that will spur her on."

"I hope so, Gil. She sounds like a nice young lady."

"They are all good kids, really, Imogen – even young Henry. Come now, let's sit and listen in to the microphones to see how they are all doing. I can't wait to find out who the winner will be."

"Me neither," Imogen said, feeling very guilty that Max had them all conned. Yes, one of the children would come away with a hundred thousand dollars, but Maximillion Crooked would be the overall winner.

TEN

ROOM ONE

*H*enry, having chosen door number one, found himself inside a very large room, which had obviously once been a bedroom. He did a quick scan of the room to ascertain what furniture was around him and where he could search. His first instinct was that there was not much to investigate and that a case of money would be large, so it would be easy to spot where it could – and could not – be hidden. His second instinct was to put his hand across his face to cover his nose and mouth. The smell in the room was vile. Surely, they could have got the cleaners in before the contestants were sent in to look around. His mother would be having a fit, watching outside, seeing the filth he was being subjected to.

He realised, however, that he could not search effectively with one hand on his face. He would have to accept the smell of urine – and God knew what else – and get on with the job. This was the first room of many he would encounter and he guessed this was possibly one of the milder smelling ones.

"You guys out there do not know how lucky you are to be out in the fresh air. It stinks in here. But hey ho! Can't spend all evening grumbling. Places to search. If I remember correctly, people used to hide their money in their mattresses in the olden days. So, that's as good a place to start as any," Henry told his watching audience.

He approached the first of what was two rows of beds, side by side along the length of the room. He did a quick calculation and realised there were twelve beds in all. So much for it being an easy room. To Henry, it seemed as though it would take hours to investigate every bed.

"Okay, here goes, everyone. I'm delving into the first mattress." It was already second nature to Henry to speak into thin air, knowing that the audiences, both outside and watching all over the US, were hanging on his every word.

"Yuck, this is horrible," he said, poking his hands into several holes in the bare and tattered bed topper. "Nothing in this one. Onto the next," he continued, as if talking to himself.

The next bed in the row was still made up with sheets and blankets. Reluctant to touch the filthy bedding, Henry extended his thumb and forefinger and pulled back the covers.

"Ahh!" he screamed and jumped away from the bed. He lost his footing and fell to the ground. Had he been able to hear the audience outside, he would have heard them all laughing. He rose to his feet and looked at the plastic snake that sat motionless upon the bottom sheet.

"Ha, bloody, ha," Henry shouted into thin air. "If that is the best you can do with your special effects, this whole competition is going to be very lame."

Henry picked up the realistic toy and threw it across the room. The mattress beneath was in much better condition than the first and Henry knew he would have to find something sharp to rip it open to investigate. He rushed to the opposite end of the room, where he could see a chest of drawers, and very conveniently found a penknife in the top draw.

"Goodness, this is just too easy. They've even planted props to help us." He returned to the second bed, made several cuts into the top and sides of the mattress, and plunged his hands inside, feeling, searching, but coming out with nothing.

"Okay, two down, ten to go. Right, bed three, here I come."

He turned around to the third bed in the row. Like bed two, it was still made up and ready to be torn apart. As before, back went the covers with one forceful tug.

"Really, very funny. Thought I would fall for it twice. Pathetic," Henry spoke into the camera, after looking at the coiled red-and-black snake that was even more lifelike than the first. He reached out his hand to pick it up – as he had with the previous one – and suddenly the snake lifted its head, turned its fearsome face to stare directly at Henry and hissed violently.

"Ahh!" he screamed again and ran from the spot as quickly as he could. Shaking and crying at the same time, his blurred vision caused him to crash into a large oak wardrobe at the other end of the room.

"What the hell," he said to himself, as he slumped to the floor in disbelief. "What a rotten trick. If that is how they are going to play, I will have to be way more careful in future. But first, I am getting the hell out of this room."

Breena closed door number two behind her and entered a peculiarly shaped kitchen. The room got wider and wider to the far end, where two other large doors with round porthole windows led elsewhere. Maybe she would head that way next, but for now, with the number of cupboards in this room, there was a lot to explore.

"Well, here we are, ladies and gentlemen. We find ourselves in our first room, which was definitely the hall's kitchen." Breena spoke as if she were presenting to a group of people in the room with her. "The first thing that strikes me is the strange design of the room. Shaped rather like a cone. It is nothing like the modern kitchens we have in our homes today. It is very basic. You will see an old tin sink on one side and a large cast-iron range on the other. The old oak dressers and cabinets seem to be intact," she said as she walked around the room, running her hands over the surfaces. "I should think, in its day, they would have been lucky to have had such a kitchen, but I guess there were lots of patients to feed. Everything is covered in dust, as you would expect, and cobwebs hang in every corner. But wait… what was that?"

Breena stood deadly still and turned to face the camera, playing to the audience beautifully.

"I heard footsteps. Is there anybody in here with me?" she asked. "I'm certain I heard something. And I can feel a strange presence around me. A cold, haunting feeling, as if someone is watching me. Well, whoever you are, I have a job to do so I am going to begin searching this room right now."

Breena opened the first cupboard. It was light enough in the room that she could see inside. Filled with tin plates, bowls and mugs, she could see there would be no room for a large amount of money. The next cupboard was filled with more of the same, so Breena decided to move to a small wooden door in the far corner. As she approached, she stopped again, appearing to listen, and then placed her hand in front of her nose.

"Crikey, it smells in here, but hang on… I hear noises again. A scratchy, scurrying noise. Let's investigate in here, ladies and gentlemen."

As she opened the tiny door, Breena quickly turned her back towards the inside of the small room and pressed her face firmly into her hands.

"God, that stinks! What on earth…?" she cried, the smell emanating from the room making her feel quite sick. "Okay, everyone, I am going to head inside. This looks like the perfect place to hide the prize money. And if they don't want us to find it, the smell is the perfect deterrent."

At thirteen, Breena was just slightly taller than the height of the door. She ducked her head under the frame and stepped inside. A quick look showed a pantry of stone walls covered with row upon row of wooden shelves. There were remains of boxes, packets and tins that had once been used to feed the inmates of the hall. The smell was like nothing Breena had ever experienced and, to her, it seemed like a mixture of sour milk, decomposing vegetables and mouldy bread.

As she stepped deeper into the space, she tried to resist the urge to leave. She noticed some large linen sacks on the floor where grain and flour had poured from them onto the ancient flagstones.

"Look here, this would be a good hiding place. I will just move these sacks to take a look behind them."

She was not sure if the audience could see into the small cubicle, although she knew they would still be able to hear her.

"Wow, they are heavy," she said as she crouched down and tried to move the first sack. The weight of it took her by surprise, and as the bag slipped from her grip and toppled over, a small, yet incredibly fast, furry creature appeared and ran towards her. She screamed as it scurried over her foot and sent her toppling backwards, her body falling back through the small doorway.

Not sure what shocked her the most, the sight of the animal or the bump to her back, she sat up and tried to compose herself. Still thinking about the audience, she tried to make light of the situation.

"There it is, folks, the first bump in the night. Now, back to these sacks." She stood up slowly, not seeing her furry friend anywhere, and went ahead with trying to move another sack. All of a sudden, it was not just one animal that took her by surprise, but a multitude. The rats – small, large, brown, white, but all very hairy – charged towards her, sending her to the ground once more.

As Breena lay on the floor, the second time in a few seconds, the mischief of rats leapt on her body. They ran up her legs, across her stomach and towards her face. They seemed to appear from everywhere as Breena wiggled and tried to shake them off.

The audience watched in horror as the furry devils attempted to complete their one mission in life: to attack their victim.

Breena yelped in pain as the beasts bit and nibbled at various parts of her body. The one thing that flashed through her mind was that if this was what a ghost hunter had to go through in search of the supernatural, then maybe it was not the career for her after all. Now, though, she was in this situation, and she needed to free herself, quickly. As she wriggled free from the small doorway, she noticed an old broom to her left. The head was almost bristleless, but the stick could be her saviour. She grabbed hold of the handle and began to beat the rats, knocking them from her body. One by one, they flew in all directions until, finally, her body was free and she was able to find her feet.

"I'm sorry, guys; if the money is in here, it will have to stay where it is. I'm out of here," she said, as she ran towards the two doors at the back of the kitchen.

Frankie was delighted to have chosen door number three. She stepped through, closed the door behind her and took an initial look around. *Nothing too sinister*, she thought. *Just a children's bedroom.* Her next thought was that she did not remember seeing this room when she had visited the hall years before. She was shocked at the idea that Hacker the Horrible had had patients that were children.

As she looked around, it quickly dawned on her what she was actually doing in the hall. Her family had been feuding over their horrific history all her life because of what her great-great-great-great-grandfather – if that was the right amount of 'greats', she was never sure – had done. Now she had to try to put it right.

She'd heard the stories about all the people that had lived and died at the hall, and it upset her terribly that children, possibly her age or younger, had been sent to such a place or even abandoned there. Although she had never lived in the stunning Hackerton family mansion, she had lived a wonderful life, wanting for nothing, and it broke her heart that people could have treated the children of a past era so appallingly.

Thoughts of the family home stopped Frankie in her tracks. She knew her mother was out with friends that evening, but she was now on live TV for the world to see. What if her grandparents or Aunt Imogen were watching? She had made it this far, but she would be in the biggest trouble of her life if they discovered her deception.

She suddenly had an image of her mother and grandfather storming their way into the hall to have her removed and she began to giggle to herself. Especially at the fact she had succeeded with her plan. She had travelled to New York and back, and now entered the hall all of her own volition and none of her family were any the wiser.

All she needed was a few more hours – just to be there and prove the place was not haunted – then everything would be all right. Maybe then, her mother could settle her differences with her grandparents, and they may even be able to move into the family home, which, of course, was her greatest wish. Frankie did not care how much trouble she got in, as long as it cured the family rift.

After a few moments contemplating her situation, she remembered, once again, that she was live on television and taking part in a game show. She remembered the cameras watching her and knew she had to play the game while she was there.

"Look at this," she said, as she moved around the long, narrow room. "Small beds like my junior bed when I was five. And these metal cribs. All with bars on the sides and leather straps around the mattresses. How sad for the children who stayed here. Nevertheless, I have a bag of money to look for."

Frankie got down on her hands and knees and looked under each of the eight beds and cots, but found nothing. So far, so good.

She moved to the end of the room and sat down on a low stool that stood in front of a small wooden dressing table.

"An old metal hairbrush – maybe they were not treated so badly, after all," she said under her breath, as she picked it up and stroked it down the length of her auburn hair.

"Mine! Leave it!" The words were very faint and quiet, but she had definitely heard them. Or had she? She placed the hairbrush down in the same spot from where she had picked it up and stood up to look around the room.

"Who's there?" she shouted. "Is that you, Breena? I'm not going to be frightened by you."

Thankfully, no response came and Frankie assumed her mind was playing tricks on her. There was no one in the room with her. She was sure of that.

The only other place to look in the room were the drawers in the dressing table. Although she was sure each drawer was too small to hide a large amount of money, she decided to look anyway. The organisers of the show could clearly be devious, so anything was possible.

After opening every drawer in turn, she found no money, as she had expected. The last drawer, however, contained several, very old, sepia photographs of children. They showed them tied to chairs, strapped into their beds, scrubbing floors on their hands and knees, and even brutally fighting with each other. The scenes were very disturbing for Frankie and she realised that this game could not be over too soon for her, as she made her way towards a different door from the one she'd entered.

Cait had wobbled on entering through door number four. As she closed the door, she stood, bolt upright, unable to move. With her back to the door, she looked around the space ahead of her. It was a small room and didn't look too daunting on first impression. She was grateful to Zach for his help in encouraging her to get started. Now, though, she wished he was still by her side. She had never been so scared in her short life. Even her audition for The New York Academy had not been this frightening.

"Okay, what have we got in here?" she whispered quietly under her breath in encouragement to herself. She shivered slightly and winced at the smell in the room.

"Some sort of office or study, I guess. Whoever worked here, it looks like they left in a terrible hurry. Books and papers everywhere. Scattered all over the floor. Hang on, recent paper coffee cups on the desk. Someone has been in here recently," she told herself, forgetting all about the audience watching her, and completely unaware that Gil and his crew had used the room a couple of months before to work on the project.

"Nothing in or under the desk," she mumbled, after a thorough search of the drawers and cupboard housed amongst the rotten wood of the old writing table.

"Right, what next?"

Feeling more comfortable and relaxed, she headed for a rickety bookcase that was barely standing. A couple of the shelves had fallen to the floor, relieving themselves of the books they held. Not wanting to cause any damage to the ones that remained, she carefully felt around them all.

"Nothing here either. Ooh… what's that?"

Cait felt another shiver run over her, as she turned to see one of the curtains moving unnaturally. She edged away slowly and waited.

"Come on, Cait, get a grip. It's probably nothing."

She moved forward, psyching herself up. Extending her hand, she slowly pulled back the dirty, ripped grey curtain and breathed a sigh of relief. A pane of glass in the window frame had been broken and the wind was gushing through, blowing the fabric.

"Thank God," she said, feeling silly for thinking it would be anything more sinister.

It was a small room and the longer Cait spent in there, the more at ease she felt and even started to forget about the smell. There was nothing left for her to search, so she bent down and began to pick up some of the books from the floor. Once she cleared the books, she noticed a small rug that had seen better days. Her inquisitive nature got the better of her and she rolled it back. A small metal ring became visible on the floorboards and Cait felt a rush of excitement flow over her.

"Now, this could be something," she spoke as she tugged at the ring.

Gradually, a square trap door opened upwards out of the floor to reveal a large cavity below. It was very dark and Cait was unable to see clearly into the space. She knelt nervously down and placed one hand into the darkness, feeling and hoping that she would come across the prize they all coveted. Firstly, to win the money, but secondly, and now more importantly, that the whole nightmare would be over.

Sadly, for Cait, the void was empty and her heart sank as she knew the terrible task of searching had to continue. Not in this room, though. She had exhausted all places to look and knew it was time to head to the next door and onto the next room.

Zach was still thinking about Cait as he closed door five. He could not shake from his mind the fear he had seen on Cait's face and hoped, above all else, that she was safe and not too scared of what this crazy, old building was going to throw at her. He even hoped that somewhere along the route he might meet up with her and, with his help, they could complete the quest together. He knew that was not in the rules, but he couldn't imagine anyone entering the house to stop them. For now, though, he had a job to do and that was to search this large, open space, which contained a desk, a chaise longue and a filing cabinet.

He could not see what purpose the room held. With its lack of amenities and furniture, he could only think that it had been used as some sort of anteroom or chamber. As it was next to the entrance foyer, it was perfectly situated to place waiting visitors without allowing them to see any further into the hall.

"Right, ladies and gentlemen, I find myself in a fairly large room of not much significance. It is a strange shape and contains not much of anything in the way of furniture to explore. It has no windows; it smells old and musty and has three more doors leading off in the other corners. Nothing too strange at first glance. Maybe they are breaking us in gently. Or maybe I just got lucky." Zach moved towards the chaise longue and sat down, producing a cloud of dust around him as he did so.

"Yuck, this room could do with a good clean, but I guess that is what happens when a place is left unused for a hundred years."

He sat quietly for a moment, then spoke again.

"I really hope Cait and the others are having as easy a time as I am. I would hate to think that they are struggling or too scared," he said out loud, as he ran his hands all over the surface of the dirty, faded fabric of the chaise longue.

He may have been in, what he considered, an easy and even boring room, but outside the audience were loving him. They loved his casual yet very natural manner; they loved his attitude; and, most of all, they loved the fact that he was more worried about the younger children than himself. Yes, Zach Hamilton was already a hit and he had barely started.

"I can't feel anything in this sofa other than the dirt across its surface. Nothing along the edges and nothing underneath," he said, as he bent his body forward to take a look. "I don't see any holes anywhere and I can't imagine they would have gone to the trouble of stitching up after themselves, but I can't afford to be complacent. Luckily, I remembered to bring my penknife along."

He reached into the pocket of his jeans and pulled out the small metal knife that could prove very useful over the course of the evening. He pressed the blade through the fabric in several places, making several long slits. Each time, he poked his hands through and checked inside the filling for anything that should not have been there. Having unfortunately found nothing, Zach stood up and moved on to the filing cabinet.

"I never thought they would make it this easy," he told the audience, after checking each of the cabinet drawers. "Nothing in here but books, some old newsletters and a tatty old bible. Okay, the desk is next."

It only took a few minutes to check under the desk, behind it and in its two drawers.

"Looks like I'm done in here. No, wait! There are pictures on the walls. I mustn't leave any stone unturned."

Zach slid the first picture sideways, which revealed nothing. The second picture was a little more awkward, so he ended up pulling it clean away from the wall.

"This room is a waste of time. There's nothing doing here. One more picture and on to the next room. Hang on, what's this? There is a small hatch behind this one."

Zach carefully placed the picture on the floor and pulled the small handle on the front of the hatch. It opened easily to reveal a pile of large rectangular pieces of paper.

"Oh my God!" Zach exclaimed, as he removed the wedge of paper and flicked it through his fingers. "Money! Oh my, it's money – and plenty of it. It is very old. Notes I don't recognise, but there must be a couple of thousand dollars here."

He sat down on the chaise longue, having emptied the small, concealed hole, and counted the money. Considering their age, the notes were in very good condition. Zach guessed that whoever put the money there had clearly forgotten about it.

"Eighteen hundred dollars. Wow! Well, we know it is not the prize money and the organisers obviously didn't know it was there. I will take it with me and hand it over at the end of the show. Now, onto room number two. Which door shall I take?"

Audiences, locally and across the country, were captivated. Everyone had watched as the five contestants had searched their first rooms and dealt with the different experiences and difficulties that Hacker Hall was throwing at them. It was very early days as far as the show was concerned and Muir was delighted for two reasons: one, that Max had hidden the money well enough that it had not been found in the first hour of the show; and two, that he had just received a phone call to inform him that early indications showed that the country was hooked. Viewing figures were in the tens of millions already and others were tuning in all the time. The House of a Hundred Doors was looking like it would be an enormous hit and Muir Mason could not have been happier.

ELEVEN

ROOM TWO

*H*enry chose a door at the opposite end of the bedroom to go through. He found himself in a long, slim room that was immediately obvious as a shower room. It was a space that contained nothing other than four walls that were covered from floor to ceiling in square white tiles and several showerheads poking out of each wall.

"Well, this isn't going to take too long to search. Typical. What a boring room! Just my luck that I found the dullest of places, with not a stitch of furniture or spots to search. God, this place is so tedious. Hey, everyone, maybe I should take a shower… that would liven things up."

Henry ran around inside the room, pretending to turn on the showers. Suddenly, he lost his footing and landed, with the loudest of thuds, flat on his back in the middle of the room. His head flew back and hit the floor very hard. For a few seconds, there was no movement from him.

Outside, the audience let out a shocked gasp. Henry's mother was almost having kittens and screamed at the top of her voice for someone to get in there and help her baby. Thankfully, her distress was short-lived. Slowly but surely, everyone watched as Henry groaned and carefully sat up, rubbing the back of his head.

"Bloody hell. What just happened?" Henry spoke angrily, forgetting for a moment that millions of people were watching him. Still in pain and shocked from the fall, he sat for a while and composed himself. Once his eyes refocused, he turned his body to look back at where he had slipped and noticed a huge puddle of water in the middle of the floor.

"What on earth? How can that be? A pool of water. I don't understand; I didn't turn the showers on. I was only pretending. God, my head hurts," he said, speaking to himself.

Still sitting on the floor, not hurrying to get back to his feet, Henry noticed a pile of smashed tiles on the floor that he was certain had not been there before. Also, several broken ones had appeared on the narrow wall at the far end of the room. As he looked more carefully where the tiles had fallen, it looked as if the wall had moved slightly forward on one side. Henry, still on his knees, crawled to the end of the room and placed his fingers into the gap and pulled.

"Wow! Another room hidden behind the wall. This place just gets weirder and weirder." Henry finally got to his feet and fully opened the door to reveal a smaller room, containing a tin bath and what he could only imagine was an ancient toilet, made from a wooden box. As well as the hidden door Henry had just accessed, there were another two exits from the small bathroom. It dawned on him that, at any moment, whether one was bathing, showering or using the toilet, staff and other patients could enter from all angles. Henry was not the most sensitive of souls, but even he was upset at how the lack of privacy must have affected everyone.

"Crikey, you can't even pee in private. I am beginning to really hate this place. Thank God for my private bathroom in my suite at home," he said, not caring anymore what he said in front of the cameras. "I'm going to get out of here and see what else I can find. There has to be something more exciting for me to look at and I certainly won't find the money in here either. I'm out of here."

Henry walked cautiously back across the shower room, careful to avoid the puddle of water that had already caused him to have a large lump on the back of his head. He exited through a different door and found himself in a stairwell. Two flights of stairs. One led up and the other led down.

"Okay, which way? Eeny, meeny, miny, moe – don't fancy down, so up I go."

Breena burst through the double doors at the back of the kitchen, making sure they were tightly closed behind her. There was no way she wanted the sharp-toothed little critters following her. She looked around and saw that she was in an extremely large, square room. Compared with the foyer and the kitchen, it looked as though – once upon a time – it would have been a very attractive room. The walls were covered in wooden panels that had green and gold velvet wallpaper on them. The floor was carpeted, which was the first she had seen, and even the remains of an elegant crystal chandelier hung from the high ceiling in the centre of the room.

"Oh, guys, look at this room. Not only is it huge, but it is pretty – in an old-fashioned kind of way. There does not seem to be much in here for me to investigate, but it sure is a lovely room. I would like to think they held parties and balls here for the residents, but I doubt it somehow, so I can't imagine what they used it for. At least I am away from the kitchen, and let's hope there are no rats in here or I think I will scream. Talking of those evil little beasts, my legs are sore. They must have got me, good and proper," Breena told the audience as she sat down on the carpet and rolled her jeans up to her knees.

She had a few scratches on her left leg and a couple of small puncture wounds on her right. They had bled slightly, but all in all, the cuts were not too bad.

"Thank heavens for the thickness of denim. It must have saved me. Just a couple of cuts," she said, taking a tissue from her jacket pocket, which she licked and patted against her leg to clean away the blood.

"Right, onwards with the task at hand. Let's see what this room has in store for me," she told everyone and jumped to her feet after rolling her trouser legs back down.

She moved around the room slowly, taking everything in, and ran her hands over the softness of the wallpaper. "This stuff they have covered the walls with is so nice. I might ask my grandma if they still make it. I wouldn't mind it on my walls – but enough of that, the money can't be here and the only things to look through are the stacks of chairs in the corner. Sorry, everyone watching, I seem to have picked a very uneventful room. Short of ripping up the carpet, the chairs are my only bet."

Breena moved across to the opposite side of the room and looked up at several columns of stacked, old wooden chairs, with velvet fabric on the cushioned seat pads. They towered high above her head and she worried that if she climbed up, they may all topple to the floor. Instead, she began on her hands and knees, checking between all the legs and each individual seat. Once back on her feet, she looked as high as she could without climbing, then pushed her way behind them to investigate further. As she did, her back skimmed one of the wall panels and she heard a faint click. "I don't know if you heard that out there. There was a click behind me as my back brushed the wall. It was subtle, but definitely there." Breena slid back out from the gap she had squeezed into and, as she did, a section of wall popped open.

"What have we here?" she asked the watching audience. "Looks like a secret cupboard. I don't reckon it is a door to another room.

And I don't think I can get through the gap to look inside unless I move some of the chairs."

Fortunately, the tower of chairs that blocked Breena's access was one of the smaller ones. She used every ounce of her strength to pull it forward enough to open the door wide enough, not only to fit through, but to allow the audience to see inside the space.

"Right, I'm going in," she said, still slightly out of breath from the exertion of the heavy load. "There seems to be something in here, on the floor. Wait, it looks like an old blanket, and it seems to be covered in… dried blood. Oh, my!" she said, as she bent to pick it up.

"Ahh!" she screamed, loudly, when she saw what was lying under the blanket. "It looks like the body of a baby. A girl, I would say, from the blonde, curly hair. Ooh, poor thing – that's awful."

Breena lowered herself to her knees to take a closer look and realised something was not quite right. Stretching out her hand, she poked the figure and her fingers met with a solid surface.

"Phew, it's okay, everyone. It's just a doll. Thank God," she exclaimed, with a huge sigh of relief. "After the rats, I'm not sure I could have handled a dead body, too. Well, there is nothing else in here, so I am going to cover it back up and get moving to another room."

Frankie had moved through one of the two other doors at the end of the dormitory and found herself in a hallway with stairs leading up and down. She had not heard any other voices since she had left the bedroom and stood for a few seconds deciding which way to go.

"Right, up or down? Breena told me that from a ghost-hunting point of view, the best things are always in the basement. Although nothing seems to be straightforward in this place, my gut instinct is to head down, having never been down there before. So, here I go, everyone. Come on, follow me down."

The cameras in the stairwell followed Frankie as she made her descent. As she reached the bottom and stepped through another door, she was picked up on the next camera in a dark corridor. It was the most eerie atmosphere that Frankie had felt since entering Hacker Hall and she smiled to herself.

"This looks a bit more interesting. I'm not sure what we are going to find, but I guess this is what Breena thinks ghost hunters experience. I wish you could feel how chilly it is down here. And the smell: it's almost like a mixture of a dirty farmyard and over-boiled vegetables. Come on, let's see what this place is hiding."

Frankie walked to her left and, turning a corner, found herself in another narrow hallway with several metal doors on each side. Every door was closed. Through a small, barred opening, she could just see inside if she stood on her tiptoes. Frankie knew immediately they were cells and quickly established that they were larger on one side. Having turned her back to look through the openings on the opposite side, she discovered more cells of a much smaller size.

"Crikey, you lot want to see what I have found. A whole corridor of cells. My God, I never thought they kept patients in such terrible places. I would have thought they needed love and care," she said, sliding a metal lever aside to open the first cell door. "This place is unbelievable, but I guess I am going to have to search them all. The money could be hidden anywhere down here. This first cell is just a stone floor with the remnants of dry old straw on the floor. I see what looks like a water bowl in the corner, and chains and leather straps hanging from the walls. How could they make people live like this? It's disgusting," she said, moving the straw around with one of her feet. "Well, there is nothing in here anyway, so I'm heading to the next one."

The two cells next door were slightly different inside in that the straw was gone, as were the chains. Instead, they were replaced with dirty, pale grey sections of padded fabric, which covered every inch of the walls and floors.

"These cells are even worse, guys. Just padding everywhere. These must have been for the most distressed patients. I guess they were put in these to prevent them from hurting themselves. I can understand that a little, I guess, if it was for their own safety, but there must have been better ways to look after them."

Frankie didn't even bother to go inside and turned her back to face the cells behind her.

"Oh Lord, I can't believe this. I didn't think it could get any worse down here." She opened the door of the first mini cell, which was about the size of a telephone box inside.

"Holy smoke! I'm not sure if you can see this, ladies and gentlemen. I would rather not be showing you at all. Each cell is only a couple of feet wide and deep, and there are tiny spikes sticking out from each of the walls in various places. I'm guessing the only reason they had cells like this was to punish the patients. However long they were locked in these, they would have had to stand up straight. I can see that if they moved quickly or toppled to the sides, they would have been cut or stabbed. I have never been so shocked or saddened by anything in my life," she said, having looked briefly in each of the four box cells, knowing the patients suffered at the hands of her great-great-great-great-grandfather. "I am really not happy about any of this. I'm going to move back the way I came to see what is around the other side."

Heading back the way she came, Frankie turned right when she passed the entrance to the stairwell. The space was darker than ever; the atmosphere, more oppressive than she had previously experienced. Finally, she came across one door where she could not go any further in any direction.

"What have we here? It looks like I may have hit a dead end with this door, but you never know in this place. Okay, in I go."

Slowly, she lifted the metal latch and pushed back the heavy, oak-panelled door. As the door swung back, a dim light cast shadows over the room and Frankie let out the loudest scream she could muster. Never imagining she would see what her eyes were now showing her, she turned on her heels and ran from the room. Crying and shaking all over, she stumbled the whole length of the corridor in front of her and away from the dungeon of hell.

If Frankie had been outside, she would have heard every member of the live audience scream at the exact moment she did. Each and every one of them felt terrified, as they watched the dead body swinging from the noose, attached to the dungeon ceiling.

Cait left the office through the only other door in the room, at the opposite end from where she had entered. She was relieved that she had made it through the first room with very little trouble. She wished she had found the money and wondered how Zach and the other children were doing. Of course, as all the contestants did, she wanted to win the money, but she hoped that as soon as it was found, someone would find her, whatever room she was in, and get her out of this god-forsaken building.

Shutting the office door behind her, Cait now found herself in a room roughly the same size. It was not what she was expecting at all and she assumed that it had once been used as some sort of medicine room or store. Yet again, there was an old wooden desk and chair in one corner, and the rest of the room was taken up with row after row of grubby, white wooden cabinets attached to the walls. Most of them had glass doors, some with cracked panes, and they all contained either dozens of small, brown glass bottles with white labels on, or slightly larger clear jars with contents that Cait could not make out from where she stood. The only other pieces of furniture were two white metal cabinets on wheels. They were shaped like old-fashioned writing bureaux and Cait knew they were used to transport medication around, as she had seen something similar being used in the hospital in New York, when she had visited her mum there when she had been unwell.

"There does not seem to be too much to trouble me in here either," she told the audience, as she moved forward and began to look through the desk. Quickly satisfied there was nothing to find there, she moved on to the medicine cabinets.

"They both seem to be locked, so hopefully the sort of place the money could be hidden. I wonder how I will get into them," she asked herself – and everyone watching.

She pulled and poked the front openings and quickly concluded that a key would be needed. Thankfully, something caught Cait's eye and she looked up high above her head to see a small white box attached to the wall, just below the ceiling.

"I see a small box. Maybe it will have something inside that will help me. They obviously put it so high to keep it out of the way."

She pulled the chair from behind the desk and climbed up.

"This is great. Just what I was looking for," she said, finding the box full of old, rusty keys in many different sizes. "One of these must fit. I'll get them down and try them all."

Cait lifted every key from the hooks in the box, placed them in her pocket and carefully climbed down from the chair. She tried them all, until she found the ones that unlocked both medicine cabinets. They were filled with charts, forms, thermometers, old-fashioned syringes, bottles of dried-up ink and small glass bottles that would have contained various types of medicine, but no money.

"Oh well, another dead end. I hope the others are having more fun than I am. I am beginning to find this whole evening a waste of time and wonder if they have us on a wild goose chase. Another useless room. I can't imagine the money can be in the cupboards on the wall – they are too shallow. But I'm here, so I'd better take a look, just in case."

Cait replaced the chair behind the desk and moved closer to the walls. She had not got close enough before now to see what the jars contained. Sadly, on inspection, she was horrified to see various body parts, including fingers, toes, eyes and ears, encased within what she suspected was a formaldehyde solution. Cait realised these organs and body parts must have been taken from patients and suddenly she began to feel quite sick.

"Come on, Cait, you can do this," she said, quietly to herself, trying to psyche herself up. "Just one more cupboard and this room is done."

Taking a few deep breaths, Cait composed herself and moved to the last cupboard. She leant her head in close and opened the door, believing that she saw something move.

"This place is really getting to me now. My eyes seem to be playing tricks on me. Oh no, there it is again. There are definitely things moving in some of the jars. What on earth…?"

Cait reached her hand forward and lifted one of the suspect jars from the shelf.

"Oh my!" she exclaimed. "This one looks like it has spiders in it. It can't be." She held the jar up close to see inside more clearly. She was shocked to see hundreds of black spiders staring back at her.

"Ahh!" she shouted and dropped the jar, which smashed to the ground in front of her, releasing the contents to run free over her feet and up her legs.

Startled, Cait fell forward, crashing into the cupboard and sending the remaining jars smashing to the floor. The scene was chaos. Not only were there now spiders to contend with, but beetles and cockroaches, as well as the human body parts, all set free.

Wailing, Cait shook her legs and tried to brush away the army of creepy-crawlies that were now invading her body. Crunching noises sounded underfoot as she moved and crushed many of the nasty critters. It was not enough to stop them all, unfortunately, and as she frantically brushed them from her body, Cait ran screaming from the room.

His jacket pockets bulging from the wads of money, Zach entered a large L-shaped room that, unlike the room before, was instantly recognisable. Obviously once a lounge room, he suspected it had been used for patients and not doctors. It was a mishmash of furniture. None of the pieces matched, with odd sofas, wooden rocking chairs and winged, high-back armchairs, all designed in different patterns and fabrics. The sort of things Zach had often seen for sale in the town antique shop. The main difference being that these were dirty, tattered and smelt foul.

"Right, as before, there is plenty in here for me to explore – and my knife is going to come in very handy once again. There is a lot of furniture in here. It could take quite a while to check everywhere. Okay, I'd better get on with it. Into the first sofa, I go."

He pressed his penknife into the back of the sofa nearest to where he had entered. He made a long slit and pulled back as much fabric as he could. Having felt inside and found nothing, Zach did the same with the cushions.

"Nothing in this sofa. On to the next," he spoke, into the air.

As he began to rip open the second sofa, Zach turned back to look at the first. He felt a shiver run over his body and something made him turn his gaze behind him.

"That's odd. The cushions on that sofa have been flattened. Just as if someone has sat on them and squashed all the air out. I don't remember sitting on it… but maybe I did."

Zach shook off the strange feeling and went about attacking the remaining pieces of furniture. A fair amount of time passed and, exhausted from the constant cutting, ripping and searching, he sat in one of the rocking chairs to catch his breath. He could still feel a chill in the room and, for some reason, sensed he was not alone. For an instant, his eyes began to feel heavy. If it hadn't been for a loud bang that seemed to come from the next room, Zach would have certainly dozed off. A picture fell from the wall exactly where the noise came from and he hoped that it did not mean trouble for any of his compatriots. He stood up from the chair where he had been sitting and moved to the fallen picture to investigate. As he did, the chair he had vacated began to rock slowly, back and forth. Then, the other rocking chairs followed suit, one at a time, until they were all swinging, as if someone were sitting in them.

"Okay, that's it. I don't know what the hell is going on in this room, but enough is enough," Zach told the audience, as he ran towards a door at the opposite end of the room.

The contestants had been in the house for two hours. The live audience was still enthralled by everything they were seeing. Their admiration for the strength and commitment of the children was growing with every moment. In the control room, though, Max was anything but enthralled. With every minute that passed, he was getting more and more impatient, and more and more angry. Someone had better find his money and they had better find it soon.

He decided to take a quick break. Maybe a few minutes out of the hall would calm him down. He left via the back door. Locking it behind him, he headed to the production trailer where he knew Imogen and Gil were listening to the show.

"Hello, lovebirds. Everything all right?"

"We are okay, Max," Imogen replied, ignoring his flippant comment. "How is it going in there? No progress yet then?"

"Nothing yet, but it is such fun," Max said, through gritted teeth. "The kids are searching well and starting to witness some very peculiar things. It is wonderful to think that at the end of the evening someone is going to be rich."

Imogen looked away, so Gil could not see her face. She knew exactly what Max meant.

TWELVE

ROOM THREE

*H*enry's little rhyme had finished with his finger pointing to the upward flight of stairs. He began his ascent and noted that there was nothing of interest for him to look at or investigate on the way. He was very disillusioned with the competition so far, having been in – what he thought were – two very boring rooms with little or nothing to get his teeth into. And, of course, no prize money.

"Maybe I should be heading down instead," he told the listening audience. "I bet in a place like this all the good, gory stuff happened in the basement. Never mind, it's upstairs I go… and what goes up must come down. So, plenty of time to search the cellar later."

The rest of the stairwell proved uneventful and once at the top Henry was presented with three doors. The first looked different from the other two. Two were the same as all the previous doors, so he knew they were internal. The third was a solid metal door, with a small window covered in metal bars and a series of huge metal bolts.

Henry stepped forward and tried each of the bolts from the bottom upwards. The one at the top was too high for him to reach, but it made no difference anyway, for there was no moving any of them.

"Wow, these things are so stiff. Probably a hundred years of rust and dust gluing them shut. Must be some sort of exit to the outside," he said, rubbing away a small amount of dirt in order to see through the glass.

"Definitely an outside door. Looks like there is a set of stairs leading down. Must be a fire exit. That surprises me. In this god-awful place, I would have thought they'd have left the patients to die if there had been a fire. Well, I can't open it anyway, so through one of the internal doors I go."

Henry chose the door opposite the fire exit, stepped through into blackness and closed the door behind him. A second later, a light flashed on, illuminating the whole room and showing what looked like a casual sitting room. The light only lasted a few seconds, however, and Henry was suddenly thrown back into darkness. "Oh, come on, guys, get it together. What is going on with the lights? How on earth am I supposed to search if I can't see anything? Mind you, from the quick glimpse I caught, it looked like another dull-as-hell room. Perhaps I should have headed to the basement, after all."

With split-second timing, as Henry finished his sentence, the lights burst into action again. Now Henry was no longer in the boring sitting room. "What the...? This is more like it. I don't know how much you can see on the cameras out there, but this is incredible."

Henry stepped forward away from the door and moved deeper into the room. Only now, it was not a room. He found himself in a dimly lit forest, trees and undergrowth for as far as his eyes could see. There was a layer of mist covering the ground, not allowing him to see any pathway. For the first time since he had entered the house, he could smell fresh air.

"This is amazing. The special effects in this place are mind-blowing. It even smells like woodland. Well done, production team.

You really pulled this one out of the bag," Henry said into the air, as he moved deeper and deeper into the space. "This place looks as though it goes on for miles. I can't imagine where I am supposed to look for the money. It is just trees, trees and more trees," Henry added, as he travelled further from the door through which he had entered. "Maybe this is one of those rooms where they just put in the special effects to jazz up the whole experience, but leave nowhere to search out the money. Just my luck, another dud room. Well, at least it is a little more exciting than the shower room and the bedroom."

Having walked for a while, continuing to keep the audience updated on his adventure, Henry realised he was far from where he had entered and had no way of remembering where the exit was.

"Jeez, this place is infuriating. The trees and bushes feel so real when I touch them. The dampness in the air and the smell of the dew on the bark – it's all so lifelike. But now I have been here for a while, the fun is over. It's time to get out of here."

Henry began to get more frustrated as he walked around in circles for what seemed like an eternity. "Okay, a little help here wouldn't go amiss. How about giving a guy some guidance as to where the next door is?" he shouted at anyone who could hear him. Then, he stopped in his tracks and listened.

"What was that?" he shouted. "Did you lot out there hear that?"

Henry stood frozen to the spot from fear of the noise he thought he had heard. The watching audience heard it, too, but none of them believed the show would produce such a daring and terrifying twist – especially not with children. They were, however, very wrong. The sound of the howling grew louder and louder, and as Henry heard the rumble of the long-toed paws pounding towards him, he knew it was real – and he knew he was in trouble.

By the time he caught sight of the wolves, it was almost too late. Viewers everywhere gasped in horror and disbelief as they watched Henry run for his life. The penetrating wails grew louder as the pack of snarling, grey beasts came closer.

Henry tried not to look behind as he ran, although it was impossible not to check how quickly the howling enemy was approaching. They were almost upon him, as sweat and tears blurred his vision. He stumbled over a log and crashed to the ground. He knew then that fortune was on his side, as from where he had fallen, he could see a small wooden door in a large tree trunk in front of him. Believing it to be his only hope, Henry quickly opened it. Yes, it was a way out and yes, within a split second, the wolves would be upon him. He scrambled on his hands and knees, praying for his life as he crawled through the door and instantly closed it behind him. As he lay in the safety of the darkness, trying to catch his breath, Henry could hear the scratching on the other side of the door as the wolves tried to reach him. He knew there and then that he would find a way out of this hellhole as quickly as possible, with or without the prize money.

Breena crossed the ballroom to the opposite side and exited through a door that led her into a smaller room, which was filled with a dozen shelves of folded fabric items. She pulled at the first couple and released a cloud of dust all over her face and body, causing her to cough violently. Once she had recovered and the air had cleared, she observed she had pulled down several old and stained cotton sheets that had once been white.

It was a tiny room and Breena felt happy that there did not seem to be much that could scare her, although she had also thought that when she was first in the kitchen and the ballroom. The pain in her leg from the rat bites seemed to be bothering her less and she set about searching the linen store. She spent some time pulling everything off the shelves. She went through piles of sheets, blankets, pillowcases, towels and even tablecloths. And when they were scattered in a heap across the floor, she searched every shelf, deep into every corner.

"Well, after the excitement of the last two rooms, I seem to have come across, probably, the most boring room in the house. It is so odd to think that all this stuff was used on the patients that lived here a hundred years ago."

It pleased Breena to learn that they had, at least, had sheets and blankets on their beds and towels to dry themselves after a bath or shower – perhaps conditions in the hall had not been too bad.

"I don't know if I need to put all this stuff back on the shelves. I feel I should. I don't want anyone to have to come in and clear away after me, but I can't imagine anyone would mind either way. There is nothing in here, anyway. Certainly no ghosts and definitely no money, so I may as well tidy up a bit and move on to the next room."

Breena picked up all the linens she had dropped during her search and piled them onto the shelves, pushing them back to prevent them falling again. She did not bother to fold them and felt she had done all she needed to. She was not there to tidy up, after all. She was there to hunt out the prize money and, hopefully, find a spirit or two. Feeling disappointed, she left the linen store through a door at the other end of the room from where she had entered. So far, she had found nothing at all.

As Breena entered the next room, she hoped for more success. It was an even smaller room that contained a tin bath and a wooden box with a hole in it, which she guessed was some sort of old-fashioned toilet. She had a quick look around and felt disappointed again at the lack of anywhere to search. As she moved through the room, something white caught her eye alongside the toilet.

"Looks like there is something here," she said, as she bent to the floor and retrieved a cotton handkerchief.

On closer inspection, she saw it was hand-stitched with the initials 'HF'. "Hey, everyone, I've found a hankie and it looks like it belongs to Henry. He must have passed through here before me. I bet he didn't find anything either. I'm beginning to think this hall has nothing to offer a prospective ghost hunter."

A second later, Breena stood up straight from where she had picked up the handkerchief. As she turned around, she came face-to-face with a mirror on the wall. As she did, she jumped out of her skin – she was staring straight into the eyes of the most haunted face she had ever seen. She moved away from the mirror and lowered her head to rub her eyes, not believing what she had witnessed.

"Come on, Breena, get it together. It was nothing. Your imagination is playing tricks on you," she said, aloud.

She lifted her gaze to look back into the mirror and was delighted to see her own reflection and no sign of the strange image. Then, taking her by surprise, she screamed as the mirror cracked from one corner to the other with a loud bang. It made her jump and her heart skipped a beat.

"Wow, I know this is what I came here for, but this is not fun. It is all so odd. The place is creeping me out. I wonder if Henry saw anything in here. Maybe I will catch up with him shortly and find out if he saw what I did. If nothing else, I can return his hankie. Maybe he went this way," she said, as she left through another door that led to a shower room. There, she avoided a large pool of water on the floor and finally found herself in a stairwell.

After Frankie fled from the dungeon, she ran back along the corridor and through a door straight ahead of her into another dark and eerie space. She was having trouble shaking the vision of the hanging body from her mind and had to keep telling herself it was just special effects for the show and not a real image. However, now she had been back in the hall for a few hours, she was no longer sure and knew that anything was possible. Still, she was determined to prove the hall was not haunted, so special effects it most certainly was.

As she began to look over the room, she knew that this was one of the worst places in the hall. She had heard the stories but had never been able to quite believe them. And she now knew why she had been forbidden to enter the basement when she had previously visited the hall. For there, set high, almost taking pride of place in the middle of the room, was what she recognised to be an electric chair. She had seen them in history books and felt disgusted at the thought that her great-great-great-great-grandfather had possessed one. She began to feel physically sick at the prospect that he may have actually used it.

"Oh my... I know you can all see on the screen what I am looking at. I find it so hard to believe that, at any time in history, this sort of torture was used. You can even see the metal cap that was put onto the patient's heads to transmit the electricity. How on earth did anyone ever think that it was okay to use an electric chair?"

Frankie tried her hardest not to look in the direction of the electric chair as she began to search the room. She had a job to do and she was going to get on with it, however awful she felt. She methodically made her way around the room, looking under two treatment beds and looking inside rips in the leather cushioning. She inspected the racks of tools still hanging from the walls, which concealed nothing; and then searched a couple of cupboards in the corner. Soon, the only place left to look was under, and behind, the electric chair itself.

As Frankie climbed onto the platform that housed the chair, she felt several tears sting her cheeks as they fell uncontrollably from her eyes. She was aware of her young body shaking and felt determined to finish looking as quickly as possible.

Having completed her search of the room and finding no money, she headed for the door – glad to be exiting. After the upset of the previous room, she was happy to be leaving this one unscathed. She had no idea how she would have handled anything else bad and hoped that someone would find the prize bag very soon so she could leave the hall once and for all. She turned the handle of the door across the room and opened it to exit.

After Cait fled the medicine room, she found herself in a stairwell. She sat down on the bottom step and spent a few moments composing herself. Having checked her body all over and thankfully finding no more creepy-crawlies, she made her way up to the next floor.

She noticed a door on her left that she suspected was a fire exit, ignored it and entered a door on her right. Inside, it looked like yet another ordinary room. A bedroom of sorts: a large, L-shaped room with one corner designed in an odd shape, which she guessed was where the full height of the foyer below was built. There was nothing much to see other than several beds, a couple of wardrobes and some bedside cabinets – all pretty straightforward, on first impressions.

"Looks like I'm fortunate with this room, ladies and gentlemen, in that I really can't see there will be too much to bother me in here. If I never see another insect again, it will be too soon. Right, well, I had better get on with it. I have come this far, which, quite frankly, has surprised me as much as all of you watching. So, here goes, room number three to explore."

Cait began at one end and carefully turned down the beds that were still covered with bedding. She looked under the mattresses of the ones that were bare. All in all, the room and its contents were in very good condition for their age. The only thing that bothered her was the layer of century-old dust that covered everything. She worked slowly, taking her time to be as thorough as she could, moving from one bed and cabinet to the next.

"Now I am getting to understand this place a little better," she told everyone, "I am feeling a little suspicious. This room seems too good to be true. It is just too easy."

After a good half an hour of searching, Cait reached the far end of the room and the final bed. "Funny. I wonder what that smell is?" she said. "Sorry, no good asking you guys – you won't be able to smell it. Gosh, it smells like something is burning. How odd."

An instant later, just as Cait had finished studying the last bed, its mattress burst into an inferno of red fiery flames. Cait screamed in surprise and moved quickly in the direction of the next bed. As she did so, the same thing happened again. Two beds alight and double the fear within Cait. The room suddenly felt very warm as the audience watched the two beds sizzle and burn. The flames caused Cait to move back along the room in the direction she had first come. As she passed each of the remaining beds, they, too, burst into flames, one by one, as if triggered by her running. By the time she reached the door, the room was a mass of flames and smoke, which caused Cait to cough and cover her face. As she opened the door, she took a last look at the devastation around her, before slamming the door shut and finding herself back in the stairwell. She ran as fast as she could to the floor above.

The sense of relief that engulfed Zach after he left the lounge was huge – until, very quickly, as his eyes adjusted, he was thrown into confusion once again.

"What on earth...? Boy, I don't understand this place. Now, I really am confused. It's very dark in here so I don't know if you can see very much on the screen, but it looks like I have exited the hall and found myself in a large cave. It's unbelievable. It's cold, it's dank, it smells of mould and I can even feel droplets of water landing on my head. I don't know how they have done it, but they have gone all out with the special effects on this one. Oh well, I had better get on with it. I guess the prize money could be hidden anywhere in here."

Zach moved deeper and deeper into the dark expanse, feeling with his hands along the rough, cool surfaces of the rocks to guide him. He felt a chill run through him as he moved further inside and was glad of his jacket for extra warmth. It was not an environment that worried Zach. In fact, he was rather fond of exploring caves and had visited many of the several thousand caves that had formed across America. It was just not what he had expected to come across inside Hacker Hall.

"This is incredible. You would never expect all this could be produced from a series of tricks and effects. Everything in here is so lifelike. The cave seems so real and I should know – I have visited a lot of caves. I inherited the fascination for them from my dad. He loved them, too. Strange coincidence that I am the one who found it."

As he walked around, it was difficult for Zach to judge how large the cavern was and if there were any places for a stack of money to be hidden. He hoped that it had just been placed in the dark and he may stumble upon it. However, having learnt quickly how hard the production team had worked to make the competition so tough and interesting, he knew they were never going to make it that easy.

Still fumbling around in the dark, Zach began to feel a little disorientated. It felt like he had been walking around for ages and had turned several corners in the cavity. The last corner, however, stopped him in his tracks. He wasn't quite sure what it was at first. It was the low-pitched groan that alerted him. All too quickly, though, it turned to a loud, full-blown roar. By the time the second roar came, it was too late. The large brown bear had seen Zach enter his lair and he was on his hind feet, standing tall, towering above Zach's head.

Not sure what to do, Zach stared, frozen for a few seconds, at the grizzly beast. He had seen in movies that it was advisable to stand your ground and show no fear. However, that was easier said than done when you were face-to-face with one. Slowly, still looking into the large, black pear-shaped eyes, he backed away, to the last corner he had come around. Once at the corner, he turned on his heels to flee, but unfortunately was met by another unpleasant surprise.

He ran straight into a cauldron of flying bats, circling in the air, clearly disturbed by the noise of the angry bear. Thousands of the furry, brown winged beasts swarmed around. Crashing into his body and face, Zach flailed his hands about him, trying to shoo them away to clear his vision. Sadly, there were just too many of them. Zach thought that he would have preferred to try his luck with the bear, rather than this army of mini flying creatures.

He retraced his steps, back in the direction he had come when he had first entered the cave, but every step was a battle, fighting his way through the bats that had nowhere to escape to in the dark space. Finally, Zach saw a small white light and headed towards it.

"Thank God, I think I may be able to see the exit. I am out of here and if the money is hidden behind that bear, it can damn well stay there. He can keep it."

The light came from behind a pile of rocks that looked like they had recently fallen from the sides of the cave, but Zach's instincts told him he was near where he had entered the room and quickly began to shift the rocks, one by one, until a door was revealed. He opened it quickly, still fighting off the last few remaining bats, and moved through, slamming the door closed behind him, leaving the bear and the bats to the confines of the cave.

Still extremely unnerved, Zach ran back the way he had originally come, through the lounge room and finally into the stairwell, where he sat, alone and shaking, and waited for the fear within him to subside.

Behind the hall, in his trailer, Muir could not have been happier. His telephone had been ringing off the hook with offers of congratulations and words of praise for the incredible show that was being aired. It was an instant success and he had already had other networks calling and asking if they could air follow-up shows in various venues of interest across the country. He certainly felt he had been on to a winner the day Maximillion Crooked had walked into his office – and now he knew he was.

Meanwhile, in the trailer next door, Imogen and Gil were getting to know each other. They had talked constantly for the past three hours, with the exception of when Max had entered briefly.

"Okay, Imogen, I think we are getting along all right and I want you to know that you can trust me. I saw the stare you threw Max when he mentioned someone getting rich tonight and I have always felt there is something more between you. If you wish to talk about it, I am here to listen and help if I can," he told her.

"Thank you, Gil, it is a kind offer – and yes, of course I trust you, but sadly, I am unable to tell you at the moment. I would dearly love to and I ask you to please trust me, too, just for a while longer. By the end of the show, I will be happy to share everything with you."

"No problem, Imogen. I trust you know what you are doing, but I am here for you if you need me. Now, things are hotting up in the hall, so let's get on with listening to the rest of the show."

THIRTEEN

ROOM FOUR

Nearly four hours had passed since the children had entered the house and the show had begun. All the members of the live audience were still captivated and enthralled, as were the viewers across the country. The same, unfortunately, could not be said for the five contestants inside the hall. Although they were working alone, it was evident they were all feeling the same way. Cracks in their behaviour were beginning to appear. Frustration, tiredness and fear had set into them and they were getting to the stage where they no longer cared who won the money. They just wanted the show to be over and to get out of the house.

The experience of the forest and being chased by wolves had terrified Henry and shaken him beyond belief. Still on the first floor, he found himself in a miniscule room. On initial glance, it looked like an ordinary space and he was grateful that he had not found himself in another room brimming over with special effects.

Henry, though, could not shake the anger that had built inside him. He had never been as frightened in his whole life as when the wolves had been after him and he was infuriated with the show's makers for putting him – and probably the other children, for all he knew – in such dangerous situations.

"Well, I seem to have found myself in a very tiny room. There are some cabinets on the walls and a couple of metal desk things on wheels. It is smaller than my bathroom at home and God knows what it was used for. But do you know what? I am past caring. It could be a bloody torture chamber, for all I care. I am sick to death of this place. You all saw what happened to me in that last room. Mason, how dare you put my life in danger like that and frighten me so badly. My father is going to be having very strong words with you when I get out of here," Henry bellowed at the camera in the corner of the room. "At this moment in time, I don't even care if I find the money. I'm even beginning to wonder if it actually exists. Maybe they just put us kids in here for the sheer hell of it – to make a TV show and make them look good. I bet there isn't even any money in the house. Look here," Henry said, as he moved towards a loose floorboard in the middle of the room, which was slightly raised above the rest of the floor.

"Look, a loose floorboard. Let's pull it up and see if the money is hidden underneath," Henry said, as he dropped to his hands and knees and pulled the board free. "See, as I thought, absolutely nothing. This would be the perfect hiding place. Wouldn't you agree, everyone? But no, absolutely nothing. Nada. Not a whistle. As I have been telling you all, no money. The competition is a con," he screamed again, into the camera.

Still on his knees, Henry found that once he had removed the first floorboard, a number more were loose. He systematically went about removing several others until he had made a hole in the floor large enough to fit his small body. "Now, see here, everyone, these floorboards came away so easily, you would think they had been taken up before. And as you can see, the hole is big enough for me to climb into," he said, lowering his body carefully into the recess, which was deep enough for him to lay flat.

"The perfect-size hole to house a case full of money, but no, it's not here and I'm pretty certain none of the others have found it either. As I said, the show is a big con and I am going to see to it that you, Muir Mason, get your just deserts for treating us this way. Mark my words, my father will make you pay," Henry shouted from the hole where he sat, shaking with anger.

In the control room, Maximillion Crooked was also shaking with anger. This haughty, spoilt young man was going to ruin everything if he did not shut up. He was clearly very distressed and frustrated that he had not found the money, but Max could not risk him getting any more out of control. If Johnson Fortune were to step in and pull Henry out of the hall, the whole show would be jeopardised and Max would never get his money.

A push and pull of a couple of buttons and, suddenly, the camera and microphone were cut from the medicine room where Henry Fortune was still sitting in his newly made hole, ranting. The video screen outside that had been following Henry's movements had turned to a blank screen and he could no longer be heard by the audiences.

"We are very sorry for the small technical problem we are experiencing in the room where you were watching Henry. We are working to correct the problem as quickly as we can, so please bear with us and we will have that room up and running as soon as possible," Max told everyone watching and listening.

No one saw Max pick up a small bag of tools, unlock the internal door, leave the control room and enter the main part of the hall. A quick run through the rooms and up the stairs, and he quietly entered the room where Henry was still exploring under the floorboards.

Ten minutes later, once he had returned to the control room, Max turned the camera in the medicine room back on but made sure he left the microphone off. "Thanks for your patience, ladies and gentlemen. We now have the problem resolved," he lied. "As you can see, that room is now empty. It looks like Henry has moved onto another room. I'm sure we will locate him and catch up with his movements soon enough."

Where Henry had chosen to climb the stairs when he entered the stairwell, Breena chose to descend them, heading down into the depths of the hall. She entered the right-hand door at the bottom of the stairs, anticipating what she might find. She knew she was heading into the basement and remembered from all the ghost adventures she had watched that the cellar was often where the action happened.

The room was in darkness as she entered, only to be thrown into some degree of light as she began to fumble around. It was a very large, almost rectangular room with black painted walls and cold, grey stone slabs covering the floor. There was a definite chill in the air, which Breena suspected was the nature of the room and, sadly, nothing more spiritual. The light was fairly dim and added to the creepiness of the space, yet Breena could easily see where she was.

"Hey, lookie here, everyone, I have found the morgue. It is the coldest room so far, but a hundred years ago they would have needed it to be. Well, I haven't caught up with Henry. He must have taken a different route from me. Never mind, I'm sure I can return his handkerchief to him when we are finished. For now, though, it's time to look around," she commented, excitedly. "From an immediate recce, there is a lot in here to search. I can see three metal tables on wheels. They have raised edges and a couple of small holes in each. Those, ladies and gentlemen, I am sure, were to lay the dead bodies on to carry out autopsies. I'm not sure that they would have needed to do autopsies on the dead patients in a place like this, but I guess that, sometimes, maybe their relatives requested them. My only hope is that they didn't just carry them out for the fun of it. Did you know, by the way, back then, they called dead bodies 'cadavers.'" Breena spoke knowledgeably to her audience as if they were in the room with her. Keeping them entertained was her ambition and that is exactly what she was doing.

"Nothing around these tables, though," she said, as she searched underneath them all. "Onto the cupboards; let's see if I can find anything in here. It's been a long evening already and I'm assuming the money has not been found yet, or someone would have come to tell me. So, search on, I must."

Before looking inside, Breena studied the strange pieces of equipment that still rested, after one hundred years, on the countertops. Holding them up to show the audience, there were forceps, knives, hammers, pliers, tweezers, scissors and scalpels. To Breena and everyone watching, it looked more like the contents of a toolbox then a medical room.

Investigating in the cupboards, she found much of the same, along with a few towels, a couple of blankets and several sheets, which may have been used to cover the floor to protect it from droplets of blood falling from the bodies.

"Oh well, nothing in here, guys, but I have left the best until last," she said, heading to the far side of the room. "Look what we have here," she said, standing and facing a wall full of small metal doors. "These twelve small doors are the openings to the cabinets that housed the dead bodies until they were removed for burial. God, this place is fascinating. I think I am going to have to open these and have a good look inside. I wouldn't put it past the organisers to hide the money in a place like this."

Breena knelt down, opened one of the doors at ground level and poked her head deep inside.

"It is very dark. I think I am going to have to climb inside each of them to take a proper look. Not really my idea of fun, but here I go," she said, climbing onto the sliding table that rested on the interior of the first coffin-sized mortuary cabinet.

Sliding on to her stomach, she pulled herself into the tiny compartment and was instantly out of sight of the cameras. Suddenly, as if a huge gust of wind had entered the morgue, the door where Breena had entered blew shut. There was a loud thud as the metal latch connected to lock the cabinet from the outside.

Inside, finding herself trapped in the cramped space, Breena shouted for her life, screaming, calling and pleading for someone to come to her rescue and unlock the door. From outside the cabinet, not a sound could be heard.

Frankie was still feeling rather nauseous as she went through the door between the room she exited and the one she entered. She had lost all interest in the search for the prize money and wanted, more than anything, to be out of the hall. Her aim, when she came into Hacker Hall, was to prove it was not haunted and to reunite her mother with her grandparents. Of course, she still wanted that to happen, although she now realised that being in the hall was not the answer. There was certainly plenty of terrible stuff there but as to whether or not it was haunted, Frankie was past caring. She wanted out and she would have to find another way to bring her family together.

Standing in the centre of the next room, she hoped she was heading towards a way out. Before she left, though, she could not help but have a look around. As with the last room, just one object took centre stage and, once again, Frankie was horrified. Every room she had experienced since entering the basement got more and more horrific, and her upset and loathing for her great-great-great-great-grandfather's practices grew to new heights.

Frankie eyed the large copper bath and the chair hoist sitting on the floor next to it. She guessed that the hoist would have been used to lift and lower people into the bathtub and knew instantly that it would not have been used for good. Everything about this place was pure evil and so, she assumed, was what had happened to the patients who were placed there.

Next, she witnessed a mass of different shaped and sized tools and knives, hanging from racks and resting on a cupboard top. Had she still been interested in the competition, she would have looked inside the cupboard for the prize money, but that was the furthest thing from her mind, as was the fact that an audience was still watching her every move. She made no attempt to speak or engage with them now. Every ounce of her being was captivated by the copper bathtub. Frankie felt as if it was emanating some sort of magical power and it was speaking to her, calling her to move closer towards it. Nervously, she edged forwards. Not knowing why, she felt an impulse to walk over and stand directly in front of the orange metal vessel, the nervousness within her at an all-time high.

Then, standing a few inches away, she turned her eye gaze downwards and stared into the empty receptacle. Only, it was not empty. Frankie could see that the tub was full of blood-red water and there, under the surface, was the round face of a man that, unbeknown to Frankie, was the image of 'Hacker the Horrible'. She simply saw a face that bore an incredible resemblance to her grandfather, Emerson Hackerton. The water began to move around the face, which suddenly began to change colour. First bright red, bubbling and blistering all over; then, seeping from the burn holes, bright yellow pus and blood plasma; before finally the skin turned black as charcoal and burnt to a cinder.

Frankie screamed as she looked at the frazzled face and darted backwards without turning around. She lost her footing and stumbled, crashing into the cupboard that housed the tools and knives. The next few seconds happened in a blur. The audience watched, speechless, as a large silver cleaver toppled from the countertop and glided down the side of her leg, before crashing to the floor. Another long and piercing scream escaped from Frankie's lips as she fell to the floor clutching her calf. The scream resounded around Hacker Hall, while Frankie lay, wincing in pain on the cold, hard, treatment room floor, trying to stem the blood that violently pumped from her leg.

Having run up the stairs as quickly as she could, Cait was quite out of breath. She bent down, her legs supporting the full weight of her upper body. The shock of the fire in the bedroom below had frightened her greatly, but now, as the rise and fall of her chest lessened, she realised that the show makers must have played a cruel trick on her. There was no way that the dormitory on the first floor could have been alight. In a house this old, she would have been able to feel the heat and smell the burning as the fire spread. Also, the people watching would have entered the house to get the children to safety. Yes, of course, it had to have been special effects and Cait suddenly felt really stupid for being duped. But how on earth had they done it? The flames had looked so real. And then there was the smell and the heat. *Yes, it had to have been an illusion,* she told herself, as she moved from the stairwell into a large, open expanse.

The area looked like a typical attic. A dumping ground for anything that was no longer needed on the floors below. Her first thought was that any antique dealer would be in their element, searching through the masses of old pieces of furniture, mirrors, wooden chests, filing cabinets and boxes. Her next thought was that it was a huge number of items to have to search.

"Goodness, I could be up here all night, the amount of stuff in here," she spoke into the large, echoey space. "It looks like there is another door at the other side of the room. I may just take a look through that way first and see what is beyond. I can always come back if I need to."

Cait walked through the maze of belongings and opened the next door, which revealed a long, straight corridor. "It's really creepy, guys. And I would have to guess that the other contestants haven't found their way up here yet. Everything smells really old, but then I don't suppose anyone has been up here in a very long time."

She walked along the cool corridor, wishing the organisers had at least heated the place for the evening. To her right, she passed a series of small bedrooms, each pair sharing a Jack-and-Jill bathroom. At quick glance, the bedrooms looked as though, once upon a time, they had been nicely presented, leading her to believe they had not been patients' bedrooms. Although they were now tatty and dirty inside, they reminded her of some of the rooms her friends rented near her performing arts school, which made her happy that her parents had rented a nice apartment in Harlem.

"Well, it seems I have reached the end of the attic space and there is definitely no staircase to go back down at this end, so I'm going to have to head back the way I came. I think, for now, I will go back and start searching the area I first came through. Everything there looked a bit more interesting than this end of the hall – to be honest, I don't fancy looking around any more bedrooms at the moment. The one downstairs was enough for one day. Come on, let's see what exciting stuff we can find in the other room." Always remembering the audience were watching her, Cait headed back along the corridor to where she'd first entered the attic.

She spent about half an hour searching inside cupboards and boxes, under chairs and behind the cushions of two dusty sofas. She had no idea of the time as she never wore a watch, although she knew several hours must have passed since they had entered the house. She began to feel weary. It had been a long evening, and for the first time in a while, she wondered where Zach was in the house and how his search was going. She hoped that he hadn't come across too many problems and looked forward to when they would all be back outside and could tell each other about their experiences. She sat down on one of the sofas, took a brief rest and smiled to herself, knowing that Zach would be impressed with how well she had coped with being in the hall, especially after the shaky start she'd had.

Then, in the dim light, Cait saw something in the shadows of the furthest corner. Something about it intrigued her, so she left the sofa to investigate.

"What have we here, ladies and gentlemen?" she said, as she approached. "It looks like a large trunk. The kind that ladies would have once used to store their enormous dresses on a long journey. I'm not sure if you can see it clearly. It is about a metre wide and comes up to my chest. I wonder what's in it. I don't know why but I have a strange feeling. I'm very excited to look inside," she told everyone watching, "but first I will need a chair to climb on to reach into it."

Cait grabbed an old wooden chair from close by and climbed up. She flicked the latch and leant her slim body over the top of the opening.

"I was right. Look here; a beautiful lemon taffeta dress." She pulled the garment free of the trunk, shook it out and held it up for the audience to see, before dropping it to the ground.

"And there's more. Another dress, and a man's jacket and trousers." Both followed the dress to the ground. "But wait, there is something at the bottom. I can't quite see it properly; it looks like an old leather suitcase. Oh my," she told everyone, "I am feeling really weird about this." She leant over further, reaching her arms inside the trunk. "Damn, I can't quite reach it. But if I just rest on the edge of the trunk and really try, I may just make it…"

The audience watched as Cait's feet lifted away from the chair, on which she had been standing. They heard her words trail away as her body toppled headfirst, down into the depths of the trunk. Then, to make matters even worse, she heard a bang as the lid of the truck closed on top of her and the latch locked, preventing her release.

Zach had been seated in the stairwell for several minutes, trying to get over the terror he had experienced in the cave, when he heard what sounded like a loud and lingering scream. At first, he was not sure what he had heard. The noise took him totally by surprise. Was it an alarm of some kind? Or a siren, perhaps? No, Zach was sure, it was definitely a scream – a heart-wrenching scream that meant someone, one of his friends, maybe even Cait, was in trouble. He rose to his feet, forgetting about everything he had been through in the last few hours. Someone close by was in trouble and his caring nature took over. It was Zach's instinct to help and help is what he would do.

He had a definite sense as to where the cry came from. Now, though, finding himself in the basement, Zach had no idea where he would end up. He left the stairwell and ran in the direction he believed to be right. He moved along a corridor and out the other end, where he entered the treatment room with the electric chair that Frankie had vacated a few moments earlier. As Frankie had been before him, Zach was shocked and appalled at the vision of it – but that could not be an issue now. He had to find the owner of the scream.

"Hello!" he shouted. "Is anyone around? Does anyone need help?"

"Zach, is that you? It's me – Frankie. In the next room. Quick, I'm hurt."

Zach followed the voice through the door and into the next room, "My God, Frankie, what happened here?"

"Boy, am I glad to see you. It was awful. I saw this face under the water in the tub. I tumbled and knocked into the cupboard and the knife fell."

Zach looked around to glimpse the copper tub, before kneeling on the floor, "Oh Frankie, this looks really bad. I think you are going to need some stitches."

"God, it hurts. Please try and do something to help me," she pleaded, as tears of pain rolled down her cheeks – thankful, at least, that her mother was not watching.

"I will, Frankie. Just sit still and keep your hands over the cut as best you can. I will look for something to bandage it."

He opened the cupboard, from where the knife had fallen, and quickly located an old white sheet, which he could use as a temporary fix.

"I don't think this will do the job, Frankie. It's a really deep cut, but it will hopefully hold it for a while. Now, sit tight and I will wrap up your leg as best I can. Then, when you are ready, I will try to stand you up and get you out of here."

"Oh Lord! Did you hear that, Gil? That didn't sound good. Frankie could be hurt badly. I reckon one of us should get into the house and see if she needs our help. What do you think?"

The scream had shocked Gil and Imogen, who were still listening to the show from the trailer outside. And yes, Imogen was right. It did not sound good at all.

"Sure, I agree. You don't scream like that for a paper cut. Are you okay to go to the control room and rouse Max? Then, the two of you can head into the hall and help her. In the meantime, I will get over to Muir and have him call an ambulance, just in case."

"Good idea, Gil. I'm on my way."

In the control room, Max could not believe what he and the rest of America had witnessed. Damn those bloody kids. Why couldn't they just do what was expected of them and find his money? It had been a long night and his patience was already running thin. Henry had caused all sorts of problems earlier and now it was Frankie's turn. He knew it was bad news for the show and could completely scupper his plans. At this rate, the money would never be found. Everything had been going so well and he felt that, soon enough, one of them would find it, but who knew what would happen now?

He quickly turned off the camera and the microphone to the basement treatment room where Frankie sat nursing her leg, to prevent the viewers from seeing or hearing any more of her anguish, when there was a knock on the outside door.

"Max, it's me, Imogen. Let me in. Quickly. One of the children is hurt."

As if things could not get much worse, now he had Imogen interfering, too. "Sure, just unlocking it," he replied, as he turned the key in the lock.

"It's Frankie; she sounds very badly hurt. We must get down there to see if we can help her. Gil and I have been listening. We know she is down in the basement. Come on, hurry."

"Yes, of course," he said, locking the door behind her. "I was just about to grab a first aid kit and head down to offer some assistance," Max lied. "I have also turned the camera off down there to save the audience watching her agony. We can head through the internal door. The quickest way is through the bath and shower rooms, then straight down the stairs. Come on."

"Right behind you, Max."

The pair forgot their differences for a few moments as they ran at top speed through the hall and down into the basement below. Luckily, the treatment room was the first room to the left. Max opened the door and entered to see Zach kneeling in front of Frankie, wrapping a makeshift bandage around her leg.

Max was closely followed by Imogen, who stopped dead when she saw the two children sitting on the floor.

"What the bloody hell...?" she cried.

"Oh my God. Aunt Imogen, what on earth are you doing here?"

"I could ask the same of you, young lady!"

"Would somebody mind telling me what is going on here?" Max asked, his temper beginning to fray.

"Well, I'm not sure what is going on, but this girl we all know as Frankie Hatter is my niece, Frances Hackerton."

FOURTEEN

FINAL DOOM

"I don't understand what you are doing here, Frances. What is this all about?" Imogen demanded of her niece.

"I couldn't stand the feuding between Mum and Grandma and Grandpa any longer. I thought that if I could prove the hall is not haunted, then it could be sold and they could put all the problems behind them, so we could be a family again."

"Oh, Frances, sweetheart, I am so sorry. I had no idea the whole business had affected you so badly. You must have felt very upset to go to such lengths," Imogen told her niece, as she moved towards her, knelt down and wrapped her arms around her.

"Hi, I'm Zach." It was the first time he had met Imogen. "I've tried to stem the bleeding as best I could."

"That's really good of you, Zach. Thanks for helping her. I'm just going to have a look, Frances. Sorry, I know it hurts." Imogen pulled down the temporary bandage that Zach had used and instantly the blood began to flow as Frankie winced from the pain. "Sorry, darling. This is very bad. We must get you out of here. Do you think you can walk? Zach, do you think you can help me get her up?"

"Yes, sure. Take my arm, Frankie."

"Well, this is all very nice, but enough of the family reunion." Imogen, Frances and Zach had almost forgotten Max was in the room. "No one is going anywhere."

"What are you talking about Max? She is very badly hurt. We must get her to the hospital," Imogen said, as she and Zach continued to lift Frances to her feet.

"I said, no one is going anywhere. Not until my money is found," Max yelled, reaching into his jacket pocket and pulling out a small handgun. The other three gasped.

"My God, Max. What the hell are you doing? These are children we are dealing with. You can't be serious. We must get Frances out of here."

"Shut up, Imogen. I've had just about enough of your whining. Now, all three of you sit down and let me think."

"Aunt Imogen, what's going on? Why has Max got a gun?"

"Let's just do as he says and sit down," Imogen encouraged Frances and Zach. "Our friend, Max, is not who he seems. He discovered that when Harrison Hacker owned the hall, he extorted money from his patients and their relatives. The money is supposedly hidden somewhere in the hall and he set up the competition to bring you all in to find it."

"I told you to shut up," he said, waving the gun around in Imogen's direction.

"No, Max. If you are going to treat the children this way, they need to know why."

"Why did you go along with it, Aunt Imogen?" Frankie did not understand.

"Simply because he has been blackmailing me from the very start. There are several million dollars that he wants for himself. And if I didn't go along with it, he would tell the world that Harrison Hacker was your grandpa's great-great-grandfather and his political career would be in jeopardy."

"You're a despicable rat!" Zach screamed at Max, jumping to his feet.

"Yeah, yeah. I know. What can I say? It was an opportunity too good to pass up. Now, we are going to find the money, and when we have it, you can get your precious niece to the hospital. Zach, take the bandages out of this first aid box and tie Frankie up," he said, throwing the plastic box into Zach's hands. "Nice and tight now. We don't want her going anywhere.

Zach did as instructed, while Imogen and Frances sat in silent horror. "I'm sorry, Frankie. Hopefully, we will be able to get you out of here soon. I promise we will come back for you."

"It's okay, Zach. Just find the money and we can all get out of here."

"Wise words, little girl. Just wait quietly if you know what is good for you. On your feet, Imogen, it's time to go. Zach, you lead the way. And don't either of you think about doing anything stupid. This gun is loaded, so you will be sorry if you do," he said, ushering Zach and Imogen towards the door.

Still sat in the large trunk in the attic, Cait was done with being trapped in the dark. She had called repeatedly but no one was coming to her rescue. She had no idea how long she had been imprisoned, but enough was enough. She would have to help herself.

Inside the trunk, she used one leg to push the remaining items around her to one side and stood with a stoop as best as she could. Slowly and rhythmically, she began to swing her body from one side of the box to the other. There was very little space to manoeuvre, but, with the motion of her hips and shoulders, the trunk gradually began to sway.

She could feel the rocking intensifying as her movements quickened, until, finally, the trunk toppled completely over, landing with a crash that caused Cait to thump against the side of the box and bump her head with great force. That, however, did not bother her when she saw the dim light of the attic above her head, where the latch had been released and the trunk had opened from the impact of the fall.

Free of her entrapment, Cait climbed to her feet and stretched to lengthen her body, after having been confined for what felt like hours. As she turned to move away from the trunk, she caught her foot on something, tripped, tumbled and collapsed to the floor, banging her knees to match her sore head.

As she landed, Cait felt her hands touch something soft and realised the trunk had been standing on an old rug. As the trunk had fallen, it must have moved the rug, making it ruche up and entangle Cait's foot. Her knees were both throbbing from the fall, but, once again, that was not foremost in her mind. For the second time in a few minutes, fortune seemed to be on her side.

From where the rug had moved, a large, round, silver metal ring was now visible atop the wooden floorboards. She knew that the case hidden within the trunk had revealed nothing other than that what she had perceived to be clothing, having felt for the buckles and opened it in the confines of the dark space. But now, she felt her stomach turn again as she hoped that something may be concealed below.

Cait, still on her knees, tugged at the ring. As she suspected, a hatch lifted to reveal a deep and wide void beneath. It was pitch-black in the space and Cait had no way of making it any lighter. She wished she'd had the foresight to bring a torch along; nevertheless, for now she would have to use her hands to feel around inside the space. She leant forward and plunged both hands into the hole. Her breath was short and her heart was pounding, and within moments, Cait knocked her hands against something hidden in the cavity. She temporarily held her breath as she fumbled around, feeling for something to grab hold of, when, suddenly, one of her hands touched on what felt like a handle. She pulled hard and a couple of seconds later, her hands emerged from the black space holding another old leather suitcase. It was almost identical to the one she had found in the trunk, only larger. The excitement that flooded through Cait's body was enormous and she had to remind herself to breathe again.

This time, she could just about see the fastenings that held the case closed and as she popped them open, she was almost too scared to look inside. This evening and this competition had been the most frightening and demanding thing that Cait had ever done, and having forced herself to participate, she wanted – more than anything – for the competition to be over and to leave the hall. To Cait, it no longer mattered who won the money; she just needed one of them to find it so they could all get out. She had also decided, as she had fled the flames on the floor below, that if she were the one to find the money, she would split it evenly between herself and her four fellow contestants. They had all been put through the ringer and she believed they all deserved to benefit.

Very slowly, she lifted the lid. Everyone watching was captivated by what had happened to her and that she may be about to uncover something significant. Not even thinking about the show or the audience, though, she looked down into the interior of the case and let out a gasp. "Oh my God, I don't believe it. I think I have done it. I think this might be it."

Everyone around the country watched with bated breath as Cait slowly began to unpack the contents of the case. There was jewellery containing precious stones in every colour, a pair of very exquisite silver candlesticks, several strings of pearls, a bag of what looked like antique gold coins, a couple of rolled-up oil paintings and then – the pièce de résistance – hundreds and hundreds of old yellow and black paper monetary notes, the likes of which she had never seen.

Unable to speak, Cait sat motionless, staring at the contents of the case. As tears began to form in the corners of her eyes, she couldn't hear the roars of cheers and rounds of applause that rang out across America. As she sat, in deep shock, all she could think was that the game was over and she was finally free to leave the hall.

As Cait closed and locked the case, there were no screams of excitement or congratulations to herself, just a calm air of acceptance. She did not even acknowledge that there was still an audience watching or that she had won. She stood up from where she had climbed out of the trunk and found the secret hatch, and made her way towards the stairs. As calm and collected as anyone could ever be, she descended the two flights, not even pausing where she had witnessed the inferno in the first-floor dormitory. To Cait, she was on the most important mission of the whole evening: heading back to the ground floor and out of the front door.

As Cait walked down the stairs, Max, Imogen and Zach were ascending the same staircase, moving up one floor, to arrive back at ground level. Since leaving the basement, Imogen had tried to reason with Max. She had promised to stay in the hall and help him look for the money if he let Zach go and allowed Frances to get medical assistance. Unfortunately, Max was having none of it. He waved the gun around in Imogen's direction, insisting that the more people who searched, the quicker the money would be found.

"For all we know, Max, one of the other children may have already found it."

"Not a chance, Imogen. I have been watching their every move and none of them have it. So, on we go. I know Frankie did a thorough search of the basement, so let's get started tackling the ground floor."

"But Max, please. There has to be another way."

"Imogen, just shut up and do as I tell you, and we will all walk away from this in one piece," Max shouted at his frightened captives.

Having reached the ground-floor landing first, Cait could hear the voices approaching from below. Like the other children, she had not met Imogen, but she heard Max use her name and heard him shout in a very threatening manner. Wondering what was going on, Cait quickly peeped over the railing of the downward stairs to see Zach, a woman she guessed was Imogen and Max approaching. Then, as she saw the gun in Max's hand, she knew something was wrong and that they were in trouble.

Thinking fast, she knew that if Max saw her, she would be in trouble, too, so she needed to react instantly. She thought she heard him mention looking around the ground floor and knew she had to take her chances in getting out of the way. There were two doors leading from the stairwell and Cait knew she had to choose one of them. She opened the door that led to the small medicine room she had searched a couple of hours before. Immediately, she had visions of the spiders and scorpions she had encountered there. She quickly pushed the images to the back of her mind. This was now a life-threatening situation and the creepy-crawlies were the least of her worries.

It was a small room with no real places to conceal herself. She left the door open so she could hear their approach, and as she stood silently behind it, Cait prayed that they went through the other door off the stairwell.

"No, not that door, Zach. Take the second door. The first one is a shower room. I'm pretty sure we don't need to search in there."

Cait heard the order clearly and knew now that any second the three of them would be joining her in the medicine room. Still, with one hand firmly keeping hold of the heavy suitcase, she placed her other hand over her mouth as if trying to cover the sound of her breath. A second later, in the shadows, she saw Zach as he walked through the door. Her instant reaction was to run up and hug him tightly, showing how delighted she was to see him, but she knew that would be completely the wrong thing to do. What was the right thing to do, however? She had no idea. But as Cait saw Imogen walk through the door, too, she knew the time had come to decide. It was a small room; as Zach and Imogen continued to move further into the space, Cait could sense Max entering on the other side of the door.

It was now or never. The time had come for her to help. It was a split-second decision. As Cait saw the side of Max's body pass beyond the door, the hand that had covered her mouth released itself and joined the other hand on the handle of the suitcase. Then, with one heaving, swift action, she lifted the case and swung it towards Max. It was the almightiest blow and one that Max never saw coming. As he fell in shock to the ground, the gun dropped from his hand and glided across the floor.

Meanwhile, back in the morgue, Breena was beginning to feel lightheaded as she lay on the stretcher inside the mortuary cabinet. All sorts of thoughts were starting to race through her mind. She had exhausted herself calling for help, but sadly no one had come. She thought about her fellow contestants and hoped they had not found themselves in circumstances as disastrous as she had. Then, as her eyelids began to close, her last thought was for her grandmother and how much she loved her. She regretted ever entering the competition and knew her gran would never recover from losing her.

"I'm so sorry, Gran. I love you." The words escaped from Breena's lips with a whisper, as her eyes finally closed.

As if a strange force had been waiting for her to give up, the door of the cabinet burst open, allowing the long, narrow space to be filled with fresh air and light. Breena coughed as her eyes flew open. In her head, she thought she heard the words, "Go home, Breena. You are free."

She did not need to be told twice and, with renewed vigour, crawled from the confines of the small container and rose to her feet. Slightly dizzy and still a little nauseous from her entrapment, she could not remember the quickest way from the mortuary. She took the first door she saw and found herself in a large room occupied largely by a copper bathtub.

"Breena, thank God. Over here," Frankie called from where she sat, still tied up in bandages.

"Frankie, what on earth… Are you okay?"

"Well, no, not really. I fell and cut my leg badly. But that is the least of our problems. Zach came to my rescue, but then Max appeared with my Aunt Imogen and…"

"Why is your aunt here? I don't understand."

"Forget about that for a second," Frankie said, not wanting to give anything away about her family history. "It's Max who's the problem. There is a lot of money hidden here in the hall, much more than the prize money, and Max set up the competition so he could get the money for himself. He pulled a gun on us and now he has taken Aunt Imogen and Zach, God knows where, to look for the money. If you can get me up, we must try and go for help."

Breena gently untied Frankie and lifted her slowly to her feet. She gave her as much support as she could and, together, they hobbled out of the treatment room and back up the stairs to the ground floor. Not knowing which way to go, the two young girls needed to find an exit – whether it was the front door did not matter. They just needed the quickest way out to find some help. They walked through a shower room and then a bathroom until they entered a long rectangular bedroom.

"This place is so frustrating. I thought we would have found the front door by now," Breena complained.

"I know. I remembered it was like a maze the last time I came here. Wait… I think I hear something, coming from the next room."

"I hear it too, Frankie. This way. Come on."

Through the next door, the girls entered a dark, square room, filled with video screens, keyboards, buttons, levers and more equipment than either of them could have imagined.

"Great, a door that looks like an exit," Breena declared, letting go of Frankie's arm and running to open it. "It's locked. I can't believe it – just our luck."

"Don't worry about the door. Look what we have here. All this stuff must be the controls for the show. These screens show rooms in the house. Some have been switched off. What do you think?"

"You look in the cupboard underneath and I will have a look at the controls," Breena said to her friend.

She pushed and pulled at some buttons. Within seconds, the blank screens and all microphones sprang back into life. Suddenly, Breena and audiences everywhere could see the now empty basement where Frankie had been tied up, before it scanned through other rooms as if looking for the youngest contestant. Then, along with what everyone else had been witnessing, Breena began to watch the small medicine room where Max was coming round at the exact same second as Zach lunged for the gun.

"Frankie, I see Zach and your aunt. Get up! You have to see this."

"No, Breena, you have to see this. Look what I have found," Frankie stood, wincing slightly, and placed a briefcase on the countertop. "It's full of money. It must be the prize money. Max must have hidden it here while we all looked for the other money."

"Blimey, how devious. But what are we going to do? Look, Max and Zach are fighting over the gun."

"That is not our only problem. Listen, can you hear that shouting? It sounds like Henry, but I can't see him on any of the screens. What are we going to do?" Frankie was torn and very distressed.

"Well, we don't know our way around the house, but I think we have to try and help Henry. Zach and your aunt are adults, so we have to hope they can deal with Max. Henry is lost somewhere on his own. Let's see if we can find him. Besides, I am sure everyone outside has seen what is happening so they must have called for help."

Breena and Frankie – and the case filled with the prize money – left the control room the way they had come and began to search, room to room, for Henry. Frankie, almost having forgotten about the pain in her leg, was worried for her aunt and secretly prayed that neither she nor Zach got hurt. Breena carried the money and supported her injured friend as best she could.

They found nothing on the ground floor and reluctantly made their way upstairs, hoping for more success. They left the stairwell and entered the sitting room that had earlier been portrayed as a wolf-infested forest, when, suddenly, they heard banging and shouting. Instantly recognising Henry's voice, they moved to the next room, following the sounds. Shocked and disappointed at finding an empty room, they stood, not knowing where to look next.

"I could have sworn the sounds came from in here," Breena spoke first.

"Yeah, me too."

But the sound of their voices was all Henry needed. He had heard them and, with every ounce of breath left in his body, he called for his life, "Guys, it's me, Henry. I'm trapped under the floor. Please, please get me out of here."

Luckily, Max had mistakenly left the bag of tools on the floor and Breena quickly located a claw hammer, placing it under the edge of one of the floorboards to prise it loose. Once the first board was lifted, it was easy to pull up enough boards to see Henry. He began to push from underneath and within moments, he was finally free.

"Breena, Frankie, thank you! I thought I was done for. Max is evil. He buried me under there and left me to die. We must get out of here."

"We know. He has a gun and has taken Zach and Imogen," Breena told him.

"And what about Cait? Has anyone seen her?" Henry actually seemed concerned for someone else.

"No, we haven't, but come on." In the few seconds Frankie and Breena had looked at the medicine room in the control room, any sight of Cait had been obscured by the open door. "But we must head back downstairs and try to find a way out."

Imogen and Cait stood in transfixed horror as Max and Zach fought with each other. Max had recovered quickly from the initial shock of being hit with the suitcase and had pushed his body across the floor. He reached out his arm to pick up the gun at the exact moment that Zach saw it, bending down to retrieve it for himself. The battle that followed was not a pretty one, with both men grabbing and pushing at each other. They wrestled, their two bodies locked together, swirling around the room, crashing into the walls, shouting and cursing one another. Punches and slaps ensued, with both Imogen and Cait unable to see who held the gun. The grappling continued for a long while, until suddenly the fighting was halted abruptly by the roaring sound of the gun firing somewhere between the two men.

Cait screamed in disbelief and Imogen wrapped her arms around her, trying to protect her from anything that might come their way. Neither women knew what had happened nor if Max or Zach had been hit. Cait began to cry, secretly hoping it was not Zach, and Imogen could feel her slim body shaking with fear inside her arms.

A few seconds later, a second shot rang out, louder than the first, and reverberated around the tiny room. A yelp rang out from between Max and Zach, and the two men, still with their bodies entwined, fell to the floor.

Imogen and Cait waited and watched the two lifeless bodies. Two shots; two men. What if they had both been killed? Imogen would never forgive herself for introducing Max to these wonderful, innocent children and she feared Cait would never recover from the loss of the young man she so clearly adored.

They could see Max's body had landed on top of Zach's. A deep groan emerged from the lips of one of the bodies, followed by a loud wail of pain, but Imogen and Cait had no idea which of them the noise had come from. Clearly, one of them was alive, and Cait and Imogen moved forward to see if they could help. In the next second, from underneath, Zach pushed the floppy, lifeless body of Max off him and onto the floor.

"Oh my God, Zach! You are alive. Thank heavens! I was so scared. Is Max dead?" Cait asked, still shaking from the stress of everything she had just witnessed.

"I'm pretty sure he is," Imogen said, placing her hand onto Max's neck to feel for a pulse. "So sad. I never wanted any of this to happen. Poor man, what a waste."

"None of this is your fault, Imogen. You must not blame yourself. This was all on him, and if you ask me, he got what he deserved," Zach told the two women, as he sat up and placed his hands over the front of his thigh.

"Zach, you're bleeding." Cait noticed the fresh red blood pumping out from between his fingers.

"Yeah, the first bullet caught my thigh, but I'm pretty sure it only grazed the skin. It will be fine. How are the two of you?"

"We are fine," Imogen confirmed.

"Ooh, guys, I almost forgot with everything that has happened. I found the money," Cait told them, excitedly, as she moved back to the door and picked up the case that had done the initial damage to Max.

"You're kidding, right?"

"No, Zach, I'm not kidding. This case is full to the brim of cash, jewels and all sorts."

"So, it really does exist? The stories were right, all along. I can't quite believe it. I guess that's it then. The competition is over," Imogen sounded relieved, yet still anxious. "We are very near the front door here. I will get the two of you out and then I will head back to find the others. Do you think you can walk, Zach?"

"I sure can. Come on, let's get out of this place, once and for all."

The last few minutes had proved inconceivable to the audience outside and across America, and they watched in captivated horror as the final events of the evening and the competition unfolded. Henry's mother had screamed, demanding to get someone into the hall to look for her son. Breena's grandmother was mortified and fearful for her granddaughter's life. Devasted, Muir had called an ambulance to attend to Frankie and Zach, but also the police to locate and rescue everyone as soon as was feasibly possible.

The show had initially been a huge success and the evening had started out so well. How on earth had things turned so bad in such a short space of time? Muir's mood had changed quickly from one of jubilation to one of complete anger. Not only at Max, but also at himself for missing all the signs and believing in the con man who had deceived them all. And now, as Muir prepared to stand up and make a statement to the audience and the watching millions, the sirens of the ambulance and police cars deafened everyone as they raced to the property.

As Imogen and Cait helped Zach move through the office and into the front foyer, Imogen was still thinking about Frances and getting back to the basement to rescue her. They had heard the sirens outside the property and knew that help would be with them any second now.

She need not have worried; a moment later, from one of the other five doors off the foyer, Frankie, Breena and Henry appeared.

"Frances, thank God! I've been so worried," Imogen cried, as she hugged her niece. "Henry, Breena, are you both okay?"

"We are fine, thanks. You must be Frankie's Aunt Imogen," Breena said.

"We are so glad to see you all. We will be out of here very soon."

"That's good; my leg really hurts," Frankie declared. "Oh, and by the way, I found the bag of prize money that Max had hidden."

"Yes and I found the real loot that Max had sent us in to look for." Cait held up the old leather case to show them all.

"Two bags of money? Now I'm confused. Who won the competition? And where is Max, by the way?" Henry asked.

"I don't care who won, Henry. I don't want any of the money."

"Neither do I, Cait. I never wanted it in the first place," Frankie reiterated.

Suddenly, a loud bang hit against the outside of the front door, which took them all by surprise. "It's the police. We are coming in. If you can hear us, stand clear of the door. We are about to break it down."

True to their word, the front door burst open and the police and ambulance crews appeared, ready and waiting with blankets and stretchers to assist the injured children. It had been the longest and most frightening night of all of their lives and every one of them was relieved the see the emergency services as they came to their rescue. They were safe. They were free and it was over.

Holding onto each other, they exited the front door of Hacker Hall for the last time. As they stepped off the front veranda and down onto the front path, Henry turned back one more time and asked again, "Where is Max? I still haven't seen him."

The moment Imogen and the five children were clear of the hall, a strange and supernatural phenomenon occurred across all the rooms. There had been many abnormal, unplanned events that had taken place that evening, though none of the children had realised, thankfully. Breena had been trapped in the morgue, Frankie had witnessed the body hanging from the noose and the face under the water, and Cait had contended with the fire in the bedroom. None of which had been special effects, after all. And now, as the six survivors were free, a massive power loss struck the whole building and threw the hall into darkness.

No one outside or watching across the country saw Max's dead body being dragged by an invisible force from the medicine room where it lay, down the stairs to the basement and into the morgue, where, finally, it was deposited inside one of the mortuary cabinets.

As Imogen, Zach, Cait, Frankie, Breena and Henry reached the driveway, Gil, Muir and the children's families were waiting to greet them. The relief on everyone's faces was evident as the medical crews ushered Frankie and Zach into the ambulance for treatment.

"What the hell happened in there?" Muir was frantic to find out what had gone wrong.

"Steady on, Muir. You can see they've all had a difficult evening," Gil said, placing his arm around Imogen, offering comfort.

"It's a very long story. One which I will be happy to share with you all once I know Frances and Zach are safely on their way to hospital," Imogen said, turning everything over in her head. "By the way, here are the two bags of money."

"Two bags of money? Why two? And who is Frances? Oh well, I guess it will all become clear in good time."

Inside the ambulance, Cait sat quietly holding Zach's hand until the medics told them it was time to leave.

"Can I see you again, Cait, before you head back to New York?"

"Yes, of course. How does a visit to the hospital tomorrow sound?"

"Great, it's a date. Oh, and before I forget," Zach said, putting his hands into his jacket pockets, "I found this money in the hall. Can you see Mr Mason gets it?"

After the ambulance left, the power miraculously burst into life again, flooding the grounds of Hacker Hall with light. The screens showed the rooms inside the hall were empty and back to how they had looked before the competition had begun.

It was decided that everyone involved in the show would head back to the Hackers Hollow Guesthouse where Muir would pay to put them all up for the night and give Imogen the opportunity to explain what had gone on in the hall. It would be a long and difficult story to relive but it was one that most definitely had to be told.

Muir made a brief live statement thanking everyone for coming and watching the programme, but the show was over and the House of a Hundred Doors was closed for good.

The crowds were quickly dispersed by security and taxis arrived, ready to transport Muir and everyone involved in the show to the guesthouse.

"Just before you leave, Mr Mason," said one of the police officers who had first entered the hall. "We have done a thorough search of the building, and as far as we can see, there is definitely no one left inside. There is certainly no sign of Mr Crooked."

"That is odd." Imogen had been certain of his demise. "I guess he will turn up eventually. Will you please keep me updated?"

"Yes, of course, sir. Have a good evening."

A good evening? An ironic thing to say, really. Muir smiled to himself as he looked back at the hall for the last time. He waited for everyone to climb into their taxis. As he opened the door to get into his, he heard Henry say, "Why won't anybody tell me where Max is?"

EPILOGUE

HACKERS HOLLOW, 2014

*E*xactly one year after the live show had been aired at Hacker Hall, a small, select group of people gathered in the garden, as far from the building as was possible within the grounds: Emerson Hackerton, the newly appointed Senator of Pennsylvania and his wife; his daughters, Imogen and Astrid, and his granddaughter, Frances; Muir Mason and Ferdinand Gillespie; Zach Hamilton and his mother; Cait Luu, with her parents and newly arrived grandparents from Hong Kong; Johnson and Madeline Fortune and their son, Henry; and Breena Mathis and her grandmother, Mrs Carney.

There were also members of the press and media – journalists and reporters from across the country, representing both radio and television – and a squad of security guards. Lastly, a demolition team were also in attendance.

"Thank you all for coming," Senator Emerson Hackerton addressed the group. "You have been welcomed here, today, one year on from the live television game show that took place inside the hall, for two reasons. Firstly, to say farewell and witness the destruction of this ancient, regretful building. And secondly, on a far happier note, to welcome the announcement of a new project that it is my great honour to be part of as your senator. With enormous thanks for generous contributions from Mr Muir Mason and Mr Johnson Fortune, along with the legacy that was left here at the hall by my great-great-grandfather, Harrison Hacker, it gives me immeasurable pleasure to launch the Hacker Children's Foundation."

An architect's image of a gleaming, modern building appeared on a screen, which had been set up where the group sat. A round of applause burst from the hands of the gathered visitors. Emerson Hackerton raised his own hand, in order to continue.

"Work will begin immediately on this very site, and one year from now I invite you all to join me back here for the opening of the foundation's first venture. The image you now see depicts a state-of-the-art facility to offer accommodation and sports therapy for up to one hundred of Pennsylvania's disabled and deprived children. We are fortunate to be joined here today by Mr Zachary Hamilton, who has agreed to complete his bachelor's programme in sports locally and will head up the foundation's activities department, along with the assistance of Miss Cait Luu, who will lead an extensive dance programme. It is a wonderful initiative, one which my family and I are incredibly proud to be a part of. And, on that note, I would like to thank the people of Hackers Hollow and Pennsylvania for their continued support, and for their forgiveness and understanding over a dark and remorseful period in my family's history. Now, without further ado, if you would like to follow me, we will say goodbye to the House of a Hundred Doors and hello to the Home of a Hundred Children."

Cheers rang out, followed by another round of applause, as Emerson Hackerton and everyone assembled moved towards a large yellow box with a red button on it.

"Senator Hackerton! Please, stop!" The foreman of the demolition team ran towards the group.

"George, yes, what on earth is the matter?"

"We were doing a last, thorough check of the inside of the hall and I am sad to inform you that we discovered a body in one of the old cooling cabinets in the morgue."

"My God! Do you have any idea who it is?" the senator asked.

"Yes, sir, I'm afraid we do. We found a wallet in one of the pockets of the rotting jacket. I'm sorry to say that it is Maximillion Crooked."

A gasp of shocked horror escaped from the lips of everyone gathered. Imogen wobbled and Gil placed his arm firmly around her waist to stabilise her. Zach took hold of Cait's hand to show his support and she leant her head on his shoulder. Frances placed her hands over her eyes as if trying to block out the image.

"Are you okay, darling?" Gil whispered to Imogen, quietly.

"I can't believe it. I was not very fond of the man, but I would never have wished that on him. To think that for all this time, after his body vanished from the house, we all thought he had just upped and left the building, disappearing from our lives. How horrible. Do you have any idea how he got in there, George?"

"No, miss. It all seems to be a mystery. We can't piece together how he got into the morgue after the cameras stopped rolling – but it explains why the police couldn't find him after the show."

"It sure does," Gil confirmed.

"Well, it is a sorry state of affairs, indeed, but we must not allow it to darken our day and the good work that will be carried out here in the future." Emerson Hackerton wanted to rally the group. "George, have you removed the body?"

"Yes, sir."

"And the building is definitely clear?"

"It most definitely is."

"Excellent. If you could please see that the body gets to the coroner's office, I will head along there later today."

"I certainly will, sir. Now, are you ready?"

"Yes, I believe we are."

Senator Emerson Hackerton, along with his family and friends, moved once again towards the yellow box. Standing in front of it, he placed his finger on the red button.

"Okay, the building has been injected with a supply of explosives. So, if you are all ready, let's count down and close the door on Hacker Hall, once and for all. And remember, everyone, to shout 'Bang!' Here we go. Five, four, three, two, one."

And as the great-great-grandson of 'Hacker the Horrible' pressed the red button, the deafening noise that exploded through the air was met with emotional shouts of "BANG!"

ACKNOWLEDGEMENTS

The idea for this book would not have been possible without the previous existence of a 19th century hospital-asylum close to where I grew up on the boarders of Chigwell. As a young girl I would walk our family dogs across the grounds of the captivating, yet haunting building and I always wondered what life must have been like for the inmates. The facility has long since closed although the memories have never left, which inspired me to let my imagination run riot and reach my own conclusions.

A debt of gratitude is owed, once again, to Sue Boyd-Wallis - dear friend and proof-reader of all my work. Thanks for being the first to read this piece.

My heartfelt appreciation to my husband, Michael, for backing me every step of the way – guiding, supporting and encouraging at every turn.

Last but by no means least, my greatest thanks to Jeremy Thompson and the whole team at The Book Guild for all their hard work to publish this novel and for having faith in me. Hopefully there will be many more to follow.

With love and thanks, Sam x

OTHER TITLES AVAILABLE

Sophie Spirit and the Batting Manor Mystery
Published by Stanhope Books

Sophie Spirit, a deaf girl of unusual appearance, due to a rare medical condition, has spent her whole young life in London.

Unexpectedly, she finds herself living in a country village where she meets Humphrey, son of Lord and Lady Beaumont. It quickly becomes apparent that Humphrey will not be the only child she meets, when she is visited by three spirits who, when alive, were the children of the Beaumont's ancestors.

Strange things begin to happen, and all too soon Sophie finds herself entangled in a scary and devilish plot to strip the Beaumont's of the only life they have ever known.

Join Sophie as she experiences spooky, unnatural goings on and seeks to help Humphrey and his family combat the evil working against them …

Sophie Spirit and the Tower of London Treasure
Published by Stanhope Books

For her second adventure, Sophie Spirit finds herself back in London, looking after Mr Franklyn, who has fallen ill.

By coincidence, Humphrey, visiting his new London school at the same time, allows the two friends the opportunity to meet up.

Keen to share the London she knows and loves with her best friend, Sophie takes Humphrey to the Tower of London, and whilst experiencing the splendour of the magnificent landmark, things are not all they seem.

Join Sophie and Humphrey as, once again, they experience ghostly characters and stumble upon a dangerous and daring plot to steel a collection of ancient treasures from The Tower. Can the duo save the day and save the treasure?

Meanwhile, back at Mr Franklyn's home, things there too are not all they seem, and in spooky conclusion and the pair come face to face with someone they never dreamt of meeting ....

Saving Shrin Gala
Published by Stanhope Books

Mary Bridges, owner of Hawthorns Home for Foundling Children, is the only mother that Reggie Davenport, Seamus O'Donnell, Paxton Day and Jasmin Dharlia have ever known.

After receiving the devastating news that their home must close, the four best friends and D-vision members, are whisked away on a holiday of a lifetime. Unfortunately, when disaster strikes, D-vision find themselves in a strange, secret civilisation where they become drawn into a plot that threatens to destroy Shrin Gala and all its inhabitants.

Travel with Reggie, Seamus, Paxton and Jasmin to the far reaches of the world, where they must work together and combine their special abilities to battle, overcome the enemy, and find their way back to Mary...